LATIN *FOR THE* NEW MILLENNIUM

STUDENT WORKBOOK

Second Edition LEVEL **1**

LATIN FOR THE NEW MILLENNIUM
Series Information

LEVEL ONE

Student Text, Second Edition

Student Workbook, Second Edition

College Exercise Book, Levels 1 and 2

Teacher's Manual, Second Edition

Teacher's Manual for Student Workbook, Second Edition

ENRICHMENT TEXTS

From Romulus to Romulus Augustulus:
Roman History for the New Millennium

The Original Dysfunctional Family:
Basic Classical Mythology for the New Millennium

LEVEL TWO

Student Text, Second Edition

Student Workbook, Second Edition

Teacher's Manual, Second Edition

Teacher's Manual for Student Workbook, Second Edition

ENRICHMENT TEXTS

From Rome to Reformation:
Early European History for the New Millennium

The Clay-footed SuperHeroes:
Mythology Tales for the New Millennium

LEVEL THREE

Student Text

Teacher's Manual

ENRICHMENT TEXTS

Latin 3: Select Latin Enrichment Readings

ELECTRONIC RESOURCES

www.lnm.bolchazy.com

www.bolchazy.com/ebooks.aspx

Quia Question Bank

LATIN *FOR THE* NEW MILLENNIUM

STUDENT WORKBOOK

Second Edition LEVEL **1**

Milena Minkova and Terence Tunberg

Bolchazy-Carducci Publishers, Inc.
Mundelein, Illinois USA

Series Editor: LeaAnn A. Osburn

SECOND EDITION
Volume Editor: Donald E. Sprague
Contributing Editor: Laurel Draper

FIRST EDITION
Volume Editors: Elisa C. Denja, LeaAnn A. Osburn
Contributing Editors: Timothy Beck, Donald E. Sprague, Vicki Wine
Cover Design & Typography: Adam Phillip Velez
Cover Illustration: Roman Forum © Bettmann/CORBIS

Latin for the New Millennium
Student Workbook, Level 1
Second Edition

Milena Minkova and Terence Tunberg

Bolchazy-Carducci Publishers, Inc.
1570 Baskin Road
Mundelein, Illinois 60060
www.bolchazy.com

Printed in the United States of America
2017
by United Graphics

ISBN 978-0-86516-808-4

CONTENTS

PREFACE

This workbook contains exercises to be used with every chapter of *Latin for the New Millennium*. If you finish a chapter and then do all the exercises in the workbook linked to that chapter, your grasp of the material in each chapter will be stronger.

There are several types of exercises in this workbook.

- Some exercises require only that a noun(s) be declined or that a verb(s) be conjugated. You should try to do these exercises from memory in order to check your mastery of forms.

- The second exercise in each chapter of the workbook, like the second exercise in each chapter of the textbook, is devoted to English words derived from their Latin ancestors.

- Other exercises in various formats (e.g., fill-in-the blank, change given forms to another specified form, etc.) are designed to give you practice with manipulating the forms of Latin and thereby allow you to gain a greater facility with the language.

- Various types of translation exercises are found in this workbook: Latin to English translation, English to Latin translation, and translation of phrases. These exercises allow you to determine how well you can use all the forms of Latin together.

- Exercises based on new passages of Latin literature give you additional practice with the way Roman authors wrote.

- Comprehension exercises allow you to see the progress you are making at understanding written Latin.

- At the end of each chapter in the workbook, you will find a series of Content Questions related to each chapter. Be sure to answer all the Content Questions as a way to check your mastery of the material.

At the end of this workbook you will find the same English to Latin glossary and Latin to English glossary that is in your textbook. These are included in the workbook for your convenience as you do the exercises.

MM & TT
2017

CHAPTER 1

▶ EXERCISE 1

Identify the part of speech of the word in bold in each sentence. The Reading Vocabulary may be consulted.

1. Rhēa Silvia **fīliōs** amat.   _____

2. Amūlius Rōmulum et Remum **in** aquam pōnit.   _____

3. Mars Rhēam Silviam **amat**.   _____

4. Agricola **fīliōs** cūrat.   _____

5. Lupa Rōmulum et Remum **bene** cūrat.   _____

6. Nauta aquam **et** terram amat.   _____

Mars, god of war and father of Romulus and Remus.

▶ EXERCISE 2

Choose the response that completes the statement, answers the question, or means the same as the bolded word(s).

1. My **affectionate** little neighbor certainly lived up to her name.

    a. Sophia   b. Victoria

    c. Bella   d. Amy

2. Who would belong to an **agrarian** society?

    a. sailors   b. farmers

    c. doctors and dentists   d. senior citizens

3. The city **aquatics** director is in charge of the

   a. public gardens.

   c. swimming pools.

   b. tennis courts.

   d. baseball fields.

4. Which of the following describes a person performing filial duties?

   a. Sam, who cuts grass for his neighbor

   c. Joe, who tutors students after school

   b. Agatha, who takes her mother to doctor appointments

   d. Noreen, who babysits the children on her block

5. A sailor measures distance in _____ miles.

   a. English

   c. nautical

   b. Roman

   d. international

6. A **werewolf** reputedly has a(n) _____ cast to its features.

   a. lupine

   c. piscine

   b. equine

   d. serpentine

7. Which dogs gained their name from being used to drive game out of their holes in the ground?

   a. bloodhounds

   c. collies

   b. greyhounds

   d. terriers

8. Which word is **NOT** derived from *terra*?

   a. terrace

   c. terror

   b. territory

   d. extraterrestrial

9. What is a **parterre**?

   a. a ghostly apparition

   c. a group that opposes anarchists

   b. an ornamental flower bed

   d. a type of bug repellent

10. Which of the following describes a person **perambulating**?

    a. Juan, who is on a walking tour

    c. Massimo, who is driving a tourist bus

    b. Hope, who is attempting to climb Mt. Everest

    d. Serena, who is on the track team

11. A student who **cares about** learning new things is _____.

    a. intelligent

    c. irritating

    b. amiable

    d. curious

12. Which of the following describes a **benefactor**?

    a. the woman who donated paintings to the museum

    c. the logging company that clear-cut the land

    b. the city council that raised utility rates

    d. the man who paid his taxes regularly

▶ EXERCISE 3

Identify whether the word in bold is the subject, predicate nominative, or direct object in each sentence. The Reading Vocabulary may be consulted. (The word *nōn* means "not.")

1. Amūlius nōn est **deus**.   _____

2. Puella **Rōmam** amat.   _____

3. **Lupa** fīliōs cūrat.   _____

4. Nauta **aquam** amat.   _____

5. **Rōmulus et Remus** Rōmam aedificant.   _____

6. **Āthlēta** ambulat.   _____

▶ EXERCISE 4

Decline the following noun.

1. *aqua, aquae,* f.

	Singular	**Plural**
Nominative	_____	_____
Genitive	_____	_____
Dative	_____	_____
Accusative	_____	_____
Ablative	_____	_____

▶ EXERCISE 5

Identify the case and number of the following nouns. For some, more than one answer is possible. Translate each form into English.

Example: terrae
genitive singular   of the land   dative singular   to/for the land   nominative plural   the lands

1. nautārum   _____

2. fīliae   _____

3. terram   _____

4. agricolīs   _____

5. poëtās   _____

6. lupa   _____

7. Rōmā   _____

8. āthlētae   _____

▶ EXERCISE 6

Identify the case and number of the following nouns. Change the singular forms into plural and the plural forms into singular. For some, more than one answer is possible.

Example: puellā
ablative singular   puellīs

1. puellae _____
2. puella _____
3. puellās _____
4. puellārum _____
5. puellīs _____
6. puellam _____

▶ EXERCISE 7

Complete the following sentences by consulting the Latin reading passage and Reading Vocabulary. Make your answers grammatically correct.

Example: Mārs <u>Rhēam Silviam</u> amat.

1. Rhēa Silvia _____ amat.
2. Amūlius _____ nōn (*not*) amat.
3. Rhēa Silvia _____ cūrat.
4. Amūlius _____ nōn (*not*) cūrat.
5. Lupa _____ ambulat.
6. Lupa _____ amat.
7. Lupa _____ bene cūrat.

Ancient coin showing Romulus and Remus with the she-wolf.

CONTENT QUESTIONS

After completing Chapter 1, answer these questions.

1. Who were the founders of Rome?

   _____

2. Name the eight parts of speech.

   _____

3. What three properties does every noun have?

   _____

4. List the names of the five cases in order.

   _____

5. What is the usual gender of nouns of the first declension?

   _____

CHAPTER 2

▶ EXERCISE 1

Fill in the blanks by writing **1** for first conjugation and **2** for second conjugation verbs.

1. habitō, habitāre, habitāvī, habitātum   _____

2. habeō, habēre, habuī, habitum   _____

3. vocō, vocāre, vocāvī, vocātum   _____

4. teneō, tenēre, tenuī, tentum   _____

5. amō, amāre, amāvī, amātum   _____

6. parō, parāre, parāvī, parātum   _____

▶ EXERCISE 2

Choose the meaning of the Latin word from which the English word is derived.

1. fable
   - a. false
   - b. ancient
   - c. story
   - d. book

2. formation
   - a. make
   - b. appearance
   - c. important
   - d. begin

3. patronage
   - a. father
   - b. donation
   - c. heir
   - d. land

4. inimical
   - a. mind
   - b. hostile
   - c. soldier
   - d. like

5. amble
   - a. travel
   - b. love
   - c. walk
   - d. drive

6. accuracy
   - a. go to
   - b. care for
   - c. why
   - d. run

7. due
   - a. timely
   - b. two
   - c. doubt
   - d. owe

8. expectant

   a. wait for   b. look at   c. be   d. breathe

9. prohibit

   a. live   b. deny   c. have   d. keep

10. inhabitant

   a. hold   b. dwell   c. native   d. house

11. narrative

   a. story   b. sailor   c. tale   d. tell

12. essential

   a. be   b. need   c. prepare   d. basis

13. parade

   a. see   b. get ready   c. order   d. care for

14. abstain

   a. stay away   b. deny   c. hold   d. mar

15. survey

   a. road   b. measure   c. land   d. see

16. disavow

   a. call   b. deny   c. pray   d. want

17. nonchalance

   a. well   b. not   c. now   d. care for

▶ EXERCISE 3

Fill in the blanks with the missing Latin personal ending or English pronoun.

	Singular		Plural	
	Latin	**English**	**Latin**	**English**
First person	–o *or* –m	_____	_____	we
Second person	_____	you	–tis	_____
Third person	_____	(s)/he/it	_____	they

▶ EXERCISE 4

Conjugate in the present tense.

1. *vocō, vocāre, vocāvī, vocātum*

	Singular	**Plural**
First person	_____	_____
Second person	_____	_____
Third person	_____	_____

2. *dēbeō, dēbēre, dēbuī, dēbitum*

	Singular	**Plural**
First person	_____	_____
Second person	_____	_____
Third person	_____	_____

▶ EXERCISE 5

Identify the person and number of each verb and give three English translations for each.

Example: vocās
second singular   you call, do call, are calling

1. amant _____

2. habēs _____

3. tenet _____

4. ambulāmus _____

5. dēbētis _____

6. cūrant _____

▶ EXERCISE 6

Fill in the blanks with the correct form of the words in parentheses.

Example:
Fīliī fābulam ___amant___ . (amāre)

1. Poētae fābulās _____ . (parāre)

2. Puella fōrmam _____ . (cūrāre)

3. Nautae aquam _____ . (amāre)

4. Puellae lupam _____ . (vidēre)

A sketch of an ancient actor wearing the mask of comedy.

▶ EXERCISE 7

Translate into Latin.

1. You are telling stories! _____

2. We call the poet. _____

3. She takes care of the daughter. _____

4. You (plural) ought to care for the fatherland. _____

5. I love Rome. _____

6. They expect the sailors. _____

CONTENT QUESTIONS

After completing Chapter 2, answer these questions.

1. Which two major Latin authors from prior to 100 BCE are discussed in Chapter 2?

   _____

2. What models did Plautus follow in his work?

   _____

3. In which principal part is the stem of the verb found? How is the stem found?

   _____

4. How do you distinguish the first from the second conjugation?

   _____

5. In what respect do the subject and the verb agree?

   _____

Roman theatre in Mérida, Spain, where a modern-day summer festival devoted to the production of ancient plays is held annually.
Mérida was founded in 25 BCE and its original name was *Emerita Augusta* from which the modern name of Mérida is derived.

CHAPTER 3

▶ EXERCISE 1

Decline the following nouns.

1. *servus, servī,* m.

	Singular	**Plural**
Nominative	_____	_____
Genitive	_____	_____
Dative	_____	_____
Accusative	_____	_____
Ablative	_____	_____
Vocative	_____	_____

2. *magister, magistrī,* m.

	Singular	**Plural**
Nominative	_____	_____
Genitive	_____	_____
Dative	_____	_____
Accusative	_____	_____
Ablative	_____	_____
Vocative	_____	_____

▶ EXERCISE 2

Choose the word that is **NOT** derived from the given Latin word.

1. *ager*

   a. pilgrim   b. agrarian   c. agility   d. peregrination

2. *amīcus*

   a. amenity   b. inimical   c. enemy   d. amicable

3. *animus*

   a. unanimous   b. animosity   c. equanimity   d. magnate

4. *casa*

    a. casino   b. cherish   c. chasuble   d. chalet

5. *domī*

    a. domicile   b. domestic   c. dormitory   d. dominion

6. *fīlius*

    a. affinity   b. affiliation   c. filicide   d. filial

7. *rīvus*

    a. rivulet   b. derivative   c. rival   d. derision

8. *via*

    a. voyager   b. visor   c. devious   d. impervious

9. *vir*

    a. triumvirate   b. virtual   c. trivial   d. virtuoso

10. *ego*

    a. egregious   b. egocentric   c. egotistic   d. egoist

11. *timeō*

    a. intimidate   b. timorous   c. timidity   d. intimate

12. *cum*

    a. composition   b. contradict   c. commander   d. conglomerate

13. *in*

    a. input   b. incarcerate   c. initial   d. innovation

▶ EXERCISE 3

Translate into Latin.

1. in the stream   _____

2. with the sons   _____

3. in the mind   _____

4. on the roads   _____

5. with the friend   _____

6. in the water   _____

▶ EXERCISE 4

In the sentences below, use an appropriate noun from the first sentence to fill in the blank with a noun in the vocative case. Then translate both sentences.

Example: Poēta fābulam parat. Exspectāmus, _____poēta_____, fābulam.
The poet is preparing a story.   We are waiting for the story, poet.

1. Puer lupam timet. Nōn dēbēs, _____, lupam timēre.

    _____

2. Fīlius domī nōn est. Tē, _____, exspectāmus.
    tē – you (accusative)

    _____

3. Vir amīcum vocat. Amīcus, _____, nōn est domī.

    _____

4. Amīcus animum bonum nōn habet. Dēbēs, _____, animum bonum habēre.
    bonum – good (accusative singular masculine)

    _____

5. Puella in agrīs ambulat. Tē, _____, domī exspectāmus.
    tē – you (accusative)

    _____

Modern actors in ancient garb.

▶ EXERCISE 5

Translate into Latin.

1. The sons do not expect Demea.
   Dēmea, Dēmeae, *m.*

   _____

2. Syrus does not fear Demea.
   Syrus, Syrī, *m.*

   _____

3. The sons ought not to live in the fields.

   _____

4. The sons walk on the roads with friends.

   _____

▶ EXERCISE 6

Translate this fable into English.

Phaedrus, a Roman author who lived during the first half of the first century CE, was a freed slave of the emperor Augustus. He wrote the first collection of fables in Latin literature that has come down to us. Phaedrus follows the plots of his Greek predecessor Aesop, but puts them in a poetic form. The fable below is adapted from the original.

Lupus et agnus in rīvō stant. Lupus superior stat et agnus īnferior. Lupus agnum vocat: "Aquam, agne, turbās."
Agnus lupum timet: "Ego, lupe, īnferior stō. Aquam nōn turbō."
Lupus: "Tē (*accusative of* tū) nōn amō."
Lupus agnum dēvorat.

_____

_____

_____

_____

_____

_____

_____

agnus, agnī, *m.* – lamb
dēvorō, dēvorāre, dēvorāvī, dēvorātum – to devour
īnferior – lower (downstream)
lupus, lupī, *m.* – wolf

stō, stāre, stetī, statum – to stand
superior – higher (upstream)
turbō, turbāre, turbāvī, turbātum – to muddy, to stir up
   (compare "turbulence")

▶ EXERCISE 7

Using the Reading Vocabulary from Exercise 6, fill in the blanks with the appropriate endings.

Example: Agnus nōn est in agr ___ō___.

1. Agn _____ est in rīv _____.

2. Agnus lup _____ nōn vocat.

3. Agnus aqu _____ nōn turbat.

4. Lupus agn _____ nōn amat.

5. Nōn dēbēs, lup _____, agnum dēvorāre.

6. Dēbēs, agn _____, lupum timēre.

The wolf and lamb face each other.

CONTENT QUESTIONS

After completing Chapter 3, answer these questions.

1. Why have Terence's comedies remained popular?

    _____

2. When is the vocative case used?

    _____

3. In what declension and what noun-type is the vocative different from the nominative? What is the ending?

    _____

    _____

4. With what word do we usually translate the genitive? With what mark of punctuation can the genitive also be translated?

    _____

5. What is a prepositional phrase?

    _____

A sketch of an ancient mask of comedy.

CHAPTER 4

▶ EXERCISE 1

Decline the following nouns.

1. *praemium, praemiī,* n.

	Singular	**Plural**
Nominative	_____	_____
Genitive	_____	_____
Dative	_____	_____
Accusative	_____	_____
Ablative	_____	_____
Vocative	_____	_____

2. *vinculum, vinculī,* n.

	Singular	**Plural**
Nominative	_____	_____
Genitive	_____	_____
Dative	_____	_____
Accusative	_____	_____
Ablative	_____	_____
Vocative	_____	_____

Armed Roman soldiers.

► EXERCISE 2

Choose the meaning of the Latin root from which the English word provided is derived.

1. revelry
   - a. wish
   - b. enjoy
   - c. war
   - d. voice

2. castle
   - a. camp
   - b. care for
   - c. make
   - d. live

3. sedulous
   - a. house
   - b. trick
   - c. give
   - d. sweet

4. premium
   - a. best
   - b. prepare
   - c. extra
   - d. reward

5. venomous
   - a. arrival
   - b. wound
   - c. poison
   - d. chain

6. embellish
   - a. war
   - b. good
   - c. add
   - d. care for

7. armadillo
   - a. armed
   - b. courage
   - c. field
   - d. walk

8. perjure
   - a. order
   - b. lie
   - c. trick
   - d. just

9. magnitude
   - a. bad
   - b. measure
   - c. large
   - d. hold

10. dismal
    - a. spirit
    - b. give
    - c. dark
    - d. bad

11. editor
    - a. trick
    - b. enter
    - c. open
    - d. give

12. entrant
    - a. hold
    - b. prepare
    - c. enter
    - d. I

13. jussive
    - a. order
    - b. expect
    - c. legitimate
    - d. tell

14. admonition

    a. from   b. give   c. have   d. toward

15. evolve

    a. down   b. out   c. to   d. against

16. inspection

    a. into   b. on   c. not   d. away

▶ EXERCISE 3

Translate into Latin.

1. I give the reward to the famous man.

    _____

2. We tell the story about the treachery to the sons.

    _____

3. They prepare the camp for the armed men.

    _____

4. We show (*mōnstrāmus*) the road to the Romans.

    _____

5. You (plural) prepare chains for bad men.

    _____

6. We do not give poison to men.

    _____

▶ EXERCISE 4

Change the noun-adjective pairs into the singular if they are plural and into plural if they are singular. For some, more than one answer is possible.

Example: virō malō
virīs malīs

1. amīcī iūstī   _____
2. bellōrum magnōrum   _____
3. rīvō magnō   _____
4. agrī magnī   _____
5. poētam iūstum   _____
6. āthlēta praeclārus   _____

▶ EXERCISE 5

Translate into Latin. The Reading Vocabulary in Chapter 4 may be consulted.

1. Pyrrhus wants to have land in Italy.

   _____

2. A deserter walks into the camp of the Romans.

   _____

3. They ought not to give the bad man a large reward.

   _____

4. Fabricius wants to have victory through legitimate war.

   _____

5. Fabricius orders armed men to walk with the deserter to the camp of Pyrrhus.

   _____

▶ EXERCISE 6

Change the noun to the correct case required by the prepositions in parentheses and then translate.

Example: vir (cum)
cum virō   with the man

1. filia (cum)   _____

2. viae (in + accusative)   _____

3. aqua (ad)   _____

4. aqua (in + ablative)   _____

5. castra (ad)   _____

6. casae (ē)   _____

7. nautae (cum)   _____

▶ EXERCISE 7

Fill in the blanks with the correct form of the adjective in parentheses and translate each sentence. The Reading Vocabulary in Chapter 4 may be consulted.

Example: Profuga est _____malus_____. (malus)
The deserter is bad.

1. Pyrrhus est rēx _____. (praeclārus)

   _____

2. Pyrrhus _____ terram in Italiā habēre vult. (magnus)

   _____

3. Virī _____ profugam vident. (armātus)

    _____

4. Fābricius victōriam _____ vult. (iūstus)

    _____

5. Fābricius virōs _____ vocat. (Rōmānus)

    _____

6. Fābricius profugae _____ praemium nōn dat. (vīnctus)

    _____

Roman leg armor, known as greaves.

CONTENT QUESTIONS

After completing Chapter 4, answer these questions.

1. In what genre of literature did Cicero excel?

    _____

2. What is the main topic in Cicero's treatise *Dē officiīs* (On Duties)?

    _____

3. In what way do the neuter nouns of the second declension decline differently from the masculine nouns of the second declension?

    _____

    _____

4. What is the case of the indirect object?

    _____

5. What is the basic rule for how adjectives must agree with nouns?

    _____

CHAPTER 5

▶ EXERCISE 1

Conjugate in the passive voice, including the passive infinitives. Translate each form.

1. *exspectō, exspectāre, exspectāvī, exspectātum*

2. *iubeō, iubēre, iussī, iussum*

	passive form of *exspectō* + English translation	passive form of *iubeō* + English translation
First person singular		
Second person singular		
Third person singular		
First person plural		
Second person plural		
Third person plural		
Infinitive		

The Kansas state seal reads, *Ad Astra Per Aspera*, "To the stars through difficulties (rough things)."

► EXERCISE 2

Choose the response that, by derivation, completes the sentence, answers the question, or means the same as the bolded word(s).

1. The **lovely** woman was well-known for her _____.
   a. intelligence
   b. wealth
   c. assistance
   d. pulchritude

2. A **miser** is _____.
   a. wretched
   b. lonely
   c. poor
   d. greedy

3. Which of the following can be described as **sempiternal**?
   a. Latin class
   b. a diamond
   c. your birthday
   d. a parade

4. The soldiers were **helped** by the _____.
   a. Veterans' Administration
   b. mandatory retirement age
   c. Ladies' Auxiliary
   d. length of service overseas

5. An **epistolary** novel
   a. deals with the past.
   b. consists of letters.
   c. is about a self-centered hero.
   d. espouses romanticism.

6. Nicoletta was such a **familiar** visitor that she
   a. moved in next door.
   b. became well-known in the neighborhood.
   c. was practically a family member.
   d. was always invited to babysit the children.

7. The **gaudy** colors of the designer's dresses
   a. were too glaring for everyday wear.
   b. were limited to sports apparel.
   c. invited a lot of criticism.
   d. gave women much joy.

8. Which of the following describes someone who is **lachrymose**?
   a. Anna, who wept for her deceased mother
   b. Ben, who was an awkward conversationalist
   c. Mary Ann, who wrote concise book reviews
   d. Georgio, who was intolerant of cow's milk

9. Although the more recent and common meaning of "purloin" is "to steal," the word originally meant _____.
   a. to cook into a paste
   b. to put far away
   c. to cleanse
   d. to obtain power mechanically

10. The noun "lunge" now refers to a quick forward movement but is derived from the Latin through an Old French word meaning _____.

   a. to attack   b. to save

   c. to lengthen   d. to fight

11. Which of the following students was exhausted by **cogitation**?

   a. Amelia, who attended a sleepover with her friends   b. Rahat, who went home after a two-hour swim practice

   c. Kurt, who spent the morning mowing lawns   d. Candy, who just finished a final exam

12. Sympathizing with her **pain**, the visitors gave their _____ to the bereaved widow.

   a. best wishes   b. condolences

   c. helpful advice   d. donations

13. The **indolent** man looked for an easy job because he wanted to avoid _____.

   a. challenges   b. long hours

   c. pain   d. tricky situations

14. All of the following are derived from *parō* **EXCEPT**

   a. apart   b. empire

   c. separate   d. rampart

15. The prefix "ab" means "away from" in all of the following **EXCEPT**

   a. abdicate   b. abduct

   c. abort   d. abacus

16. The prefix "de" means "down from" in all of the following **EXCEPT**

   a. debit   b. deform

   c. decimal   d. detract

▶ EXERCISE 3

Decline the following adjectives.

1. *asper, aspera, asperum*

	Singular		
	Masculine	**Feminine**	**Neuter**
Nominative	_____	_____	_____
Genitive	_____	_____	_____
Dative	_____	_____	_____
Accusative	_____	_____	_____
Ablative	_____	_____	_____
Vocative	_____	_____	_____

	Plural		
	Masculine	**Feminine**	**Neuter**
Nominative	_____	_____	_____
Genitive	_____	_____	_____
Dative	_____	_____	_____
Accusative	_____	_____	_____
Ablative	_____	_____	_____
Vocative	_____	_____	_____

2. *crēber, crēbra, crēbrum*

	Singular		
	Masculine	**Feminine**	**Neuter**
Nominative	_____	_____	_____
Genitive	_____	_____	_____
Dative	_____	_____	_____
Accusative	_____	_____	_____
Ablative	_____	_____	_____
Vocative	_____	_____	_____

	Plural		
	Masculine	**Feminine**	**Neuter**
Nominative	_____	_____	_____
Genitive	_____	_____	_____
Dative	_____	_____	_____
Accusative	_____	_____	_____
Ablative	_____	_____	_____
Vocative	_____	_____	_____

▶ EXERCISE 4

Keeping the same case, number, and gender replace the adjective with the one in parentheses. Translate the changed phrase. For some more than one answer is possible.

Example: praeclāram fēminam (miser)
miseram fēminam   wretched woman

1. bonās fīliās (pulcher) _____

2. bonōrum agricolārum (miser) _____

3. malīs armīs (miser) _____

4. bonae fēminae (pulcher) _____

5. praeclārōs virōs (miser) _____

6. iūstō animō (miser) _____

▶ EXERCISE 5

Change the infinitives in parentheses to the verb form required to complete the sentence. Translate each sentence.

Example: Auxilium ā bonō virō _____datur_____. (dare)
Help is being given by the good man.

1. Venēna ā malīs virīs et fēminīs _____. (parāre)

   _____

2. Auxilium ab amīcīs _____. (dare)

   _____

3. Terra ā nautīs nōn _____. (vidēre)

   _____

4. Castra ā virīs armātīs _____. (tenēre)

   _____

5. Nauta ā familiā _____. (exspectāre)

   _____

6. Patria ā puerīs et puellīs _____. (amāre)

   _____

► EXERCISE 6

Fill in the blanks with the correct form of the adjectives and translate each sentence. The Reading Vocabulary in Chapter 5 may be consulted.

Example:

Casa nōn est _____magna_____. (magnus)

The cottage is not big.

1. Animus Cicerōnis (*of Cicero*) est _____. (miser)

   _____

2. Terentia nōn est _____. (miser)

   _____

3. Fīlia Terentiae est valdē _____ et fīlius Terentiae est valdē _____. (pulcher)

   _____

4. Praemia _____ exspectō. (pulcher)

   _____

5. Fābula ā _____ fēminā nārrātur. (pulcher)

   _____

6. Virō _____ auxilium dare dēbēmus. (miser)

   _____

Statue of a Roman woman holding a baby,
just as Cicero's wife Terentia must have
held their daughter Tullia at one time.

▶ EXERCISE 7

Translate the following passage. The Reading Vocabulary in Chapter 5 may be consulted.

Terentia Cicerōnī (*to Cicero*) salūtem plūrimam dīcit.

Epistula tua, Cicero, ā mē (*me*) tenētur. Sī dolēs, doleō. Nōn sōlum tamen cōnsilia mala ā malīs virīs contrā tē parantur, sed etiam auxilium magnum ā bonīs virīs parātur. Itaque nōn dēbēmus dolēre. Nam familia nostra (*our*) nōn est misera. Epistulae tuae longae ā mē, ā fīliō, ā pulchrā fīliā exspectantur. Valē!

_____

_____

_____

_____

_____

CONTENT QUESTIONS

After completing Chapter 5, answer these questions.

1. What is the difference between the active and passive voices?

2. Where was Cicero when he wrote sad letters to his family?

3. What construction is used with the passive voice to indicate the person who performs the action?

4. What spelling difference distinguishes the declension of *pulcher* and *miser*?

5. When is the preposition *ab* used instead of *ā*?

CHAPTER 6

▶ EXERCISE 1

Write the corresponding forms of *possum* and translate both verb forms.

1. sunt   _____   _____   _____

2. es   _____   _____   _____

3. sumus   _____   _____   _____

4. est   _____   _____   _____

5. sum   _____   _____   _____

6. estis   _____   _____   _____

▶ EXERCISE 2

Match the derivative in Column A to the meaning of the Latin source in Column B from which each is derived. Some meanings may be used more than once; some not at all.

	Column A		Column B
1. _____	impossible	A.	spirit
2. _____	doctorate	B.	be able
3. _____	gist	C.	much
4. _____	remnant	D.	example
5. _____	interest	E.	prepare
6. _____	tenebrous	F.	teach
7. _____	libel	G.	letter
8. _____	farmer	H.	save
9. _____	prejudice	I.	hold
10. _____	exemplary	J.	darkness
11. _____	represent	K.	remain
12. _____	mansion	L.	free
13. _____	infirmary	M.	be accustomed
14. _____	docile	N.	lie down
15. _____	vitamin	O.	memory
16. _____	libretto	P.	to be
17. _____	alliteration	Q.	judge
18. _____	commemorate	R.	life
19. _____	affirmation	S.	book
20. _____	reservoir	T.	strengthen
21. _____	insolence	U.	trick
22. _____	obliterate		
23. _____	victuals		
24. _____	multiplication		
25. _____	obsolete		
26. _____	adjacent		

► EXERCISE 3

Translate into English.

1. Timēre nōn dēbēmus.

_____

2. Amārī dēbētis.

_____

3. Ambulāre solēmus.

_____

4. Cūrārī dēbēs.

_____

5. In viā esse dēbeō.

_____

6. In agrō esse nōn solēmus.

_____

7. Dē cōnsiliīs cōgitāre dēbent.

_____

► EXERCISE 4

Translate into Latin.

1. I am able to walk.

_____

2. I am used to being loved.

_____

3. Poets cannot always be just.

_____

4. They are not used to preparing plans.

_____

5. Rewards ought to be given to the athletes.

_____

6. We are not used to remaining in the darkness.

_____

▶ EXERCISE 5

List the transitive and intransitive verbs in this modified reading passage. The Reading Vocabulary in Chapter 6 may be consulted.

Inter Gallōs sunt virī magnī quī vocantur Druidēs. Sacra Gallōrum ā Druidibus cūrantur. Druidēs ā Gallīs valdē timentur: nam auctōritātem magnam habent, et dē virīs bonīs et malīs iūdicant. Praemia et poenae ā Druidibus dantur. Vīta Gallōrum ā Druidibus cūrātur. Propter Druidum scientiam magnam multī puerī ad Druidēs ambulant et cum Druidibus diū manent. Druidēs puerōs docent. Druidēs dē sacrīs scientiam magnam habent, sed librōs et litterās nōn amant. Nam sacra sunt magna, sī in tenebrīs iacent. Itaque sacra Gallōrum nōn litterīs, sed memoriā servantur. Druidēs scientiam magnam memoriā servant. Itaque dum Druidēs exempla docent et fābulās nārrant, puerī memoriam firmant.

Transitive

_____

_____

Intransitive

_____

_____

This relief from the second century CE shows a teacher with students. This image, found in the area of the Roman site *Noviomagus Trēvirōrum*, is frequently cited as evidence for Roman schooling. In Roman times and still today, the area, modern-day Neumagen, is celebrated for its wine production. Today the relief is housed in the Rheinisches Landes Museum in Trier, Germany.

▶ EXERCISE 6

Change the following sentences into the passive voice. The Reading Vocabulary in Chapter 6 may be consulted.

Example: Puer puellam exspectat.
Puella ā puerō exspectātur.

1. Virī magnī praemia dant.   _____

2. Druidēs puerōs docent.   _____

3. Gallī librōs et litterās nōn amant.   _____

4. Puerī memoriam firmant.   _____

▶ EXERCISE 7

Change the following sentences into the active voice. The Reading Vocabulary in Chapter 6 may be consulted.

Example: Puella ā puerō exspectātur.
Puer puellam exspectat.

1. Sacra Gallōrum ā Druidibus cūrantur.   _____

2. Virī magnī ā Gallīs timentur.   _____

3. Vīta Gallōrum ā virīs magnīs cūrātur.   _____

4. Sacra ā Gallīs servantur.   _____

Here the face of Julius Caesar depicts his worries,
cares, and concerns.

CONTENT QUESTIONS

After completing Chapter 6, answer these questions.

1. Which are Caesar's principal works?

   _____

2. What happened on the Ides of March 44 BCE?

   _____

3. Who were the Druids?

   _____

4. How are the verbs *sum* and *possum* similar in conjugation?

   _____

5. What is the difference between transitive and intransitive verbs?

   _____

6. What is a complementary infinitive?

   _____

CHAPTER 7

▶ EXERCISE 1

Decline the following phrases.

1. *longa pāx*

	Singular	**Plural**
Nominative	_____	_____
Genitive	_____	_____
Dative	_____	_____
Accusative	_____	_____
Ablative	_____	_____
Vocative	_____	_____

2. *miser amor*

	Singular	**Plural**
Nominative	_____	_____
Genitive	_____	_____
Dative	_____	_____
Accusative	_____	_____
Ablative	_____	_____
Vocative	_____	_____

▶ EXERCISE 2

Choose the response that derives from the same root as the word provided.

1. amorous

    a. maraschino   b. amortize   c. paramour   d. amoral

2. delicious

    a. dilettante   b. deleterious   c. diligence   d. delegate

3. digit

    a. dignity   b. digitalis   c. dight   d. dainty

4. domination

a. dowager   b. donative   c. dolman   d. domino

5. binoculars

a. octavo   b. occult   c. antler   d. antioxidant

6. pacify

a. peaceful   b. impeccable   c. passive   d. impair

7. seniority

a. sensible   b. senate   c. sensation   d. sentiment

8. sororicide

a. sorry   b. sorosis   c. cousin   d. course

9. verbose

a. reverberate   b. divergent   c. verdant   d. proverb

10. messieurs

a. madam   b. medical   c. mature   d. mediocre

11. perseverance

a. service   b. severity   c. several   d. servitude

12. aim

a. estuary   b. ameliorate   c. esteem   d. amenable

13. invidious

a. vigilante   b. vinegar   c. evict   d. evidence

14. putative

a. amputation   b. compunction   c. impure   d. pitfall

▶ EXERCISE 3

Translate into Latin.

1. to/for the sisters   _____

2. to/for the old man   _____

3. by means of love   _____

4. I love the sister.   _____

5. joy of peace   _____

6. words of the old men   _____

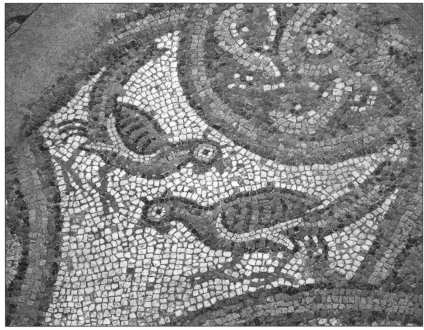
Mosaic of pheasants.

▶ EXERCISE 4

Change the following direct statements into indirect statements using the accusative and infinitive construction.

Example: Passer manet in gremiō dominae.

Poēta videt _passerem manēre in gremiō dominae._

1. Passer est dēliciae puellae.

    Poēta putat _____

2. Catullus verba senum ūnīus assis aestimat.

    Catullus nārrat _____

3. Magna praemia āthlētae dantur.

    Poēta videt _____

4. Cicero epistulās longās exspectat.

    Cicero putat _____

5. Druidēs librōs et litterās nōn amant.
    Druidēs, Druidum, *m. pl.* – Druids

    Caesar nārrat _____

▶ EXERCISE 5

In one of his poems, Catullus tells about the death of his girl's sparrow. Translate into English the following adaptation of this story.

Passer puellae est mortuus. Puella dē passere valdē dolet. Multae lacrimae sunt in oculīs puellae. Nam puella putat sē amīcum bonum nunc nōn habēre. Passer in tenebrīs ambulat. Passer ad puellam nunc ambulāre nōn potest et in gremiō puellae tenērī nōn potest. Catullus nārrat sē quoque dē passere dolēre. Nam putat oculōs puellae esse turgidōs.

_____

_____

_____

_____

_____

_____

_____

_____

mortuus, mortua, mortuum – dead
quoque – also
turgidus, turgida, turgidum – swollen

▶ EXERCISE 6

In this poem, some believe that Catullus is mocking Cicero. Translate the following adaptation of this poem into English. Then change all the sentences into indirect statements by beginning with *Catullus nārrat*.

Ego sum valdē malus poēta et Cicero est valdē bonus ōrātor. Verba Cicerōnis sunt semper pulchra. Cicerōnem tamen ūnīus assis aestimāre soleō.

Cicero, Cicerōnis, *m.* – Cicero
ōrātor, ōrātōris, *m.* – orator

Translation: _____

Indirect Statement: _____

                      _____

Translation: _____

Indirect Statement: _____

Translation: _____

Indirect Statement: _____

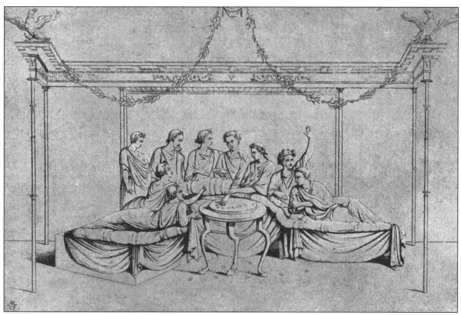

The typical number of nine diners on three couches is shown in this drawing of Romans
assembled in the triclinium for a dinner party.

▶ EXERCISE 7

In one of his poems, Catullus sends a dinner invitation to his friend, but it turns out to be quite a surprising
invitation. Translate into English.

Dēbēs ambulāre ad casam meam, Fabulle, et cēnāre mēcum. Putō nōs posse bonam cēnam habēre. Sed dēbēs
multum cibum portāre. Nam Catullus pecūniam nōn habet et nōn putat sē posse cēnam parāre. Sed Catullus
potest Fabullō mūnera pulchra dare. Itaque Catullus et puella Fabullum exspectant.

_____

_____

_____

_____

_____

_____

_____

_____

cēna, cēnae, f. – dinner
cēnō, cēnāre, cēnāvī, cēnātum – to dine
cibus, cibī, m. – food
Fabullus, Fabullī, m. – Fabullus
mēcum – with me

mūnera (acc. pl.) – gifts
nōs (acc.) – we
pecūnia, pecūniae, f. – money
portō, portāre, portāvī, portātum – to carry

CONTENT QUESTIONS

After completing Chapter 7, answer these questions.

1. To what group of poets did Catullus belong?

   _____

2. What trend in Latin literature did Catullus start?

   _____

3. With what word did Catullus and the elegiac poets after him typically describe the woman they adored?

   _____

4. What is characteristic of the nominative singular of the nouns of the third declension?

   _____

5. What kinds of verbs introduce an indirect statement?

   _____

6. With what conjunction is the indirect statement usually translated in English?

   _____

CHAPTER 8

▶ EXERCISE 1

Conjugate the following verb in the active and passive voice. Give the active and passive infinitives.

1. *dēcernō, dēcernere, dēcrēvī, dēcrētum*

Active

Infinitive   _____

	Singular	**Plural**
First person	_____	_____
Second person	_____	_____
Third person	_____	_____

Passive

Infinitive   _____

	Singular	**Plural**
First person	_____	_____
Second person	_____	_____
Third person	_____	_____

▶ EXERCISE 2

Choose the word that does **NOT** belong by derivation.

1.	a. subdue	b. duplicate	c. duchess	d. seductive
2.	a. pianoforte	b. fortress	c. effort	d. misfortune
3.	a. humid	b. homage	c. humanity	d. homicide
4.	a. militate	b. military	c. mile	d. militate
5.	a. oracular	b. suborn	c. oratory	d. adore
6.	a. realm	b. reign	c. regicide	d. reason
7.	a. temporize	b. contemplate	c. temple	d. contemplative

8.	a. timorous	b. intimidate	c. timing	d. timidly
9.	a. ascertain	b. cerebral	c. discern	d. discretion
10.	a. ditty	b. ditto	c. dictator	d. dice
11.	a. intelligent	b. collect	c. college	d. intellectual
12.	a. libation	b. liberation	c. deliver	d. livery
13.	a. navy	b. navel	c. navigate	d. naval
14.	a. appetite	b. repetition	c. competent	d. petroleum
15.	a. convict	b. invincible	c. revenge	d. vanquish
16.	a. contumacious	b. contrary	c. encounter	d. contradict

▶ EXERCISE 3

Translate into Latin.

1. we are being conquered _____

2. to be understood _____

3. it is said _____

4. you (plural) are being sought _____

5. they understand _____

6. we say _____

Xerxes with his servants.

▶ EXERCISE 4

Translate the following questions. Then choose the best answer for each and translate. The Reading Vocabulary in Chapter 8 may be consulted.

1. Quōmodo (*in what way*) Xerxēs bellum contrā Graecōs parāre dīcitur?

   Xerxēs bellum contrā Graecōs in Graeciā parāre dīcitur.

   Xerxēs bellum contrā Graecōs in nāvibus parāre dīcitur.

   Xerxēs bellum contrā Graecōs cum magnā industriā parāre dīcitur.

   _____ _____

   _____ _____

   _____ _____

2. Quō īnstrumentō (*by what instrument/means*) Graecī Persās vincunt?

    Graecī in Graeciā Persās vincunt.

    Graecī cum dolō Persās vincunt.

    Graecī mūrīs ligneīs Persās vincunt.

_____

_____

_____

3. Quōmodo (*in what way*) Graecī Persās vincunt?

    Graecī in terrā Persās vincunt.

    Graecī Persās magnā fortitūdine vincunt.

    Graecī in nāvibus Persās vincunt.

_____

_____

_____

4. Ē quā rē (*from what thing*) Athēniēnsēs līberantur?

    Athēniēnsēs timōre līberantur.

    Athēniēnsēs fortitūdine līberantur.

    Athēniēnsēs mūrīs ligneīs līberantur.

_____

_____

_____

5. Cūius reī auxiliō (*by the help of what thing*) Themistoclēs Graecōs servat?

    Themistoclēs Graecōs in templō Delphicō servat.

    Themistoclēs Graecōs in bellō servat.

    Themistoclēs Graecōs cōnsiliīs bonīs servat.

_____

_____

_____

► EXERCISE 5

Translate the following sentences, then make each one passive. The subject of the active sentence will become an ablative in the passive sentence. The Reading Vocabulary in Chapter 8 may be consulted.

Example: Cōnsilia bona Graecōs servant.
Good plans are saving the Greeks.
Graecī cōnsiliīs bonīs servantur.

Themistoclēs Graecōs servat.
Themistocles is saving the Greeks.
Graecī ā Themistocle servantur.

1. Athēniēnsēs cōnsilia Themistoclis intellegunt.

   _____

   _____

2. Persae cum multīs mīlitibus Graecōs petunt.

   _____

   _____

3. Pȳthia ōrācula dīcit.

   _____

   _____

4. Bona cōnsilia Graecōs līberant.

   _____

   _____

5. Athēniēnsēs Persās in nāvibus vincunt.

   _____

   _____

6. Dux magnus Athēniēnsēs timōre līberat.

   _____

   _____

7. Mūrī ligneī Athēniēnsēs servant.

   _____

   _____

▶ EXERCISE 6

Fill in the blanks with the appropriate ablative from the list below and translate each sentence. The Reading Vocabulary in Chapter 8 may be consulted.

litterīs   terrā   bellō   Pȳthiā   mīlitibus   templō

1. _____ līberārī et in pāce vīvere dēbēmus.

   _____

2. Graecī ā _____ Persārum petuntur.

   _____

3. Ōrācula ā _____ dantur.

   _____

4. Cōnsilium hominum bonōrum _____ servātur.

   _____

5. Themistoclēs cōnsilia Apollinis in _____ exspectat.

   _____

6. Athēniēnsēs ā _____ nāvigant et nāvēs Persārum petunt.

   _____

A view of the front of the Treasury in Delphi, Greece. Like many other cities, Athens built a treasury along the sacred path that winds its way up toward the Temple of Apollo, home of the famous Delphic Oracle. The treasury would have housed the many lavish gifts dedicated to Apollo by the city in return for the god's oracular advice. These offerings can be seen today in the Delphi Museum. The building is partly reconstructed and the white pieces are not original.

▶ EXERCISE 7

Translate the following passage into English.

The passage below is loosely based on the work of the Greek historian Herodotus (fifth century BCE) who wrote about the Persian Wars. Although Herodotus is called "The Father of History," his narrative is by no means always historically accurate.

Xerxēs est dux multōrum mīlitum. Dum mīlitēs Xerxis aquam ex rīvō bibunt, rīvus siccātur. Mīlitēs Xerxis Hellespontum trānsīre dēbent. Xerxēs dēcernit sē et virōs armātōs Hellespontum pontibus trānsīre posse. Mīlitēs pontēs aedificant. Tunc mare procellā turbātur et pontēs servārī nōn possunt. Xerxēs putat mare esse malum. Itaque iubet mare verberārī. Mīlitēs Xerxis mare verberant.

_____

_____

_____

_____

_____

_____

_____

aedificō, aedificāre, aedificāvī, aedificātum – to build
bibō, bibere, ——, —— – to drink
Hellespontus, Hellespontī, _m._ – the Hellespont, a strait
   between Europe and Asia
mare, maris, _n._ – sea
pōns, pontis, _m._ – bridge

procella, procellae, _f._ – storm
siccō, siccāre, siccāvī, siccātum – to make dry
trānsīre – to cross
turbō, turbāre, turbāvī, turbātum – to stir up
verberō, verberāre, verberāvī, verberātum – to flog, beat, whip
Xerxēs, Xerxis, _m._ – Xerxes

CONTENT QUESTIONS

After completing Chapter 8, answer these questions.

1. What sort of works did Cornelius Nepos write?

   _____

2. When did Themistocles live and what was his main achievement?

   _____

   _____

3. When may the ablative of manner be accompanied by a preposition?

   _____

4. What distinguishes the third conjugation infinitive from the second conjugation infinitive?

   _____

5. With what case is the idea of separation expressed in Latin?

   _____

6. Which form of the third conjugation is quite different from the other conjugations?

   _____

CHAPTER 9

▶ EXERCISE 1

Conjugate the following verb in the active and passive voice. Give the active and passive infinitives.

1. *sciō, scīre, scīvī, scītum*

Active

Infinitive _____

	Singular	**Plural**
First person	_____	_____
Second person	_____	_____
Third person	_____	_____

Passive

Infinitive _____

	Singular	**Plural**
First person	_____	_____
Second person	_____	_____
Third person	_____	_____

▶ EXERCISE 2

Choose the meaning of the Latin root from which the English word provided is derived.

1. armor
   a. love
   b. weapons
   c. death
   d. defense

2. chapter
   a. body
   b. book
   c. seek
   d. head

3. citadel
   a. against
   b. head
   c. citizen
   d. swift

4. corsage
   a. body
   b. heart
   c. know
   d. do

5. marinate
   a. water
   b. sea
   c. marble
   d. death

6. mortgage

    a. beg   b. carry on   c. death   d. memory

7. muliebrity

    a. woman   b. sea   c. good   d. free

8. tempestuous

    a. seek   b. feel   c. temple   d. time

9. suburb

    a. walk   b. city   c. useful   d. where

10. obedient

    a. hear   b. eat   c. good   d. give

11. miscreant

    a. body   b. believe   c. begin   d. know

12. congestion

    a. feel   b. large   c. long   d. carry

13. plebiscite

    a. know   b. beauty   c. peace   d. law

14. insensate

    a. know   b. estimate   c. feel   d. old

15. souvenir

    a. conquer   b. come   c. empty   d. poison

▶ EXERCISE 3

Decline the following phrases.

1. *pulchrum corpus*

	Singular	**Plural**
Nominative	_____	_____
Genitive	_____	_____
Dative	_____	_____
Accusative	_____	_____
Ablative	_____	_____
Vocative	_____	_____

2. *mala mors*

	Singular	**Plural**
Nominative	_____	_____
Genitive	_____	_____
Dative	_____	_____
Accusative	_____	_____
Ablative	_____	_____
Vocative	_____	_____

3. *bonum exemplar*

	Singular	**Plural**
Nominative	_____	_____
Genitive	_____	_____
Dative	_____	_____
Accusative	_____	_____
Ablative	_____	_____
Vocative	_____	_____

▶ EXERCISE 4
Translate into English.

1. sentiunt _____

2. audiuntur _____

3. marium _____

4. venīs _____

5. audīminī _____

6. urbium _____

7. scīris _____

8. audīrī _____

9. venītis _____

10. cīve _____

11. animālium _____

12. corporī _____

▶ EXERCISE 5

Translate into Latin.

1. in the sea _____

2. many examples _____

3. You (plural) are coming to the cities. _____

4. to the sea _____

5. The times are not good. _____

6. We save (our) bodies. _____

7. Joy is being felt. _____

8. (He) behaves well. _____

9. We hear the speech. _____

10. You know the deception. _____

11. The women do not believe. _____

▶ EXERCISE 6

Translate the following text into Latin.

Catiline has great courage in body and in spirit. However, the spirit of Catiline is bad and he loves bad examples. For the leader has in his mind the death of Roman citizens. Catiline knows that he does not seek peace, but seeks war. Catiline decides to conquer the Romans, but is conquered by the consul. The head of Catiline is being carried from a battle to the city.

_____

_____

_____

_____

_____

_____

Catilīna, Catilīnae, *m.* – Catiline
portō, portāre, portāvī, portātum – to carry
pugna, pugnae, *f.* – battle

During the lifetime of King Jugurtha of Numidia (160–104 BCE) this
republican denarius from 136 BCE was minted. The coin shows
the helmeted head of the personification of Roma.

▶ EXERCISE 7

Translate the following text into English.

Iugurtha magnum rēgnum in Africā habēre dēcernit et auxilium ā virīs Rōmānīs petit. Iugurtha pecūniam virīs Rōmānīs dat. Itaque Iugurtha sentit sē posse ex pecūniā multās rēs habēre. Iugurtha dīcit urbem Rōmam vēndī posse. Propter hoc Iugurtha putat mortem ad urbem venīre posse.

_____

_____

_____

_____

_____

Africa, Africae, *f.* – Africa
hoc – this
Iugurtha, Iugurthae, *m.* – Jugurtha
pecūnia, pecūniae, *f.* – money

rēgnum, rēgnī, *n.* – kingdom
rēs (*acc. pl.*) – things
vēndō, vēndere, vēndidī, vēnditum – to sell

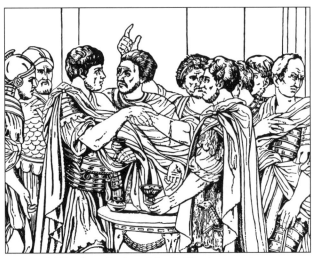

Soldiers from the time of the Catilinarian conspiracy
that eventually failed.

CONTENT QUESTIONS

After completing Chapter 9, answer these questions.

1. Where is there a slight irregularity in the fourth conjugation present?

    _____

2. In which cases are the *i*–stems different from the other words belonging to the third declension?

    _____

    _____

3. In what way are the *–ar*, *–al*, and *–e* nouns different from the other *i*–stems of the third declension?

    _____

4. What is the peculiarity of neuter nouns shared by all declensions?

    _____

    _____

5. Who was the first great Roman historian writing in Latin whose works survive?

    _____

6. Who was Catiline?

    _____

CHAPTER 10

▶ EXERCISE 1

Conjugate the following verb in the active and passive voice. Give the active and passive infinitive.

1. *iaciō, iacere, iēcī, iactum*

Active

Infinitive   _____

	Singular	**Plural**
First person	_____	_____
Second person	_____	_____
Third person	_____	_____

Passive

Infinitive   _____

	Singular	**Plural**
First person	_____	_____
Second person	_____	_____
Third person	_____	_____

▶ EXERCISE 2

Choose the response that does **NOT** derive from the Latin word provided.

1. *deus*
   a. edify   b. adieu   c. deity   d. divine

2. *dōnum*
   a. pardon   b. donor   c. madonna   d. donation

3. *equus*
   a. equestrian   b. equal   c. equestrienne   d. equine

4. *flamma*
   a. inflammable   b. flamboyant   c. aflame   d. conflagration

5. *hostis*

   a. hostel   b. hostility   c. host   d. hostile

6. *nox*

   a. nocturnal   b. equinox   c. innocuous   d. nocturne

7. *perīculum*

   a. perilous   b. experience   c. imperil   d. peril

8. *ācer*

   a. acrid   b. vinegar   c. eager   d. acute

9. *celeber*

   a. celebrity   b. celerity   c. celebrate   d. celebration

10. *fēlīx*

    a. feline   b. felicitous   c. felicitate   d. felicity

11. *fortis*

    a. enforce   b. comfort   c. fortuitous   d. reinforce

12. *aedificō*

    a. edifice   b. edify   c. edification   d. edible

13. *capiō*

    a. recovery   b. capillary   c. prince   d. municipal

14. *capiō*

    a. conceit   b. cable   c. capsule   d. concept

15. *cupiō*

    a. cupola   b. covet   c. cupidity   d. concupiscence

16. *dēleō*

    a. deleterious   b. indelible   c. delete   d. indelicate

17. *fugiō*

    a. centrifuge   b. effulgence   c. fugue   d. refugee

18. *moveō*

    a. mutiny   b. motor   c. movie   d. mule

19. *moveō*

    a. motion   b. mobcap   c. motif   d. mobile

20. *pugnō*

    a. repugnant   b. pugnacious   c. pugree   d. impugn

▶ EXERCISE 3

Decline the following phrases.

1. *hostis ācer*

	Singular	Plural
Nominative	_____	_____
Genitive	_____	_____
Dative	_____	_____
Accusative	_____	_____
Ablative	_____	_____
Vocative	_____	_____

2. *dux fēlīx*

	Singular	Plural
Nominative	_____	_____
Genitive	_____	_____
Dative	_____	_____
Accusative	_____	_____
Ablative	_____	_____
Vocative	_____	_____

3. *dōnum celebre*

	Singular	Plural
Nominative	_____	_____
Genitive	_____	_____
Dative	_____	_____
Accusative	_____	_____
Ablative	_____	_____
Vocative	_____	_____

▶ EXERCISE 4

Translate into English.

1. bona   _____

2. fēlīcēs   _____

3. cupiuntur   _____

4. capior   _____

5. puellārum fēlīcium   _____

6. hostibus fortibus   _____

7. iūsta   _____

8. fugiunt   _____

9. mīlitum ācrium   _____

10. cōnsulis celebris   _____

▶ EXERCISE 5

Translate into Latin.

1. to/for the renowned temple   _____

2. Fortunate people have many things.   _____

3. You (plural) think about the fierce soldiers.   _____

4. of the renowned city   _____

5. Just people do not think about rewards.   _____

6. Gifts are desired.   _____

7. Bad things are not always seen.   _____

8. The fortunate do not fear.   _____

9. to/for the fierce enemy   _____

Laocoön and his two sons being strangled by serpents from the sea. This masterpiece of the Hellenistic style, when discovered in the Renaissance, influenced artists like Michelangelo.

▶ EXERCISE 6

Translate the following passage into English.

Lāocoōn Trōiānus cōnsilia hostium intellegit. Equum ligneum ante portam urbis positum videt. In equō esse perīculum magnum scit. Trōiānōs dē perīculō monēre cupit. Trōiānī autem dē perīculō scīre nōn cupiunt. Equum esse dōnum pulchrum crēdunt. Itaque verba Lāocoontis nōn audiunt. Minerva Trōiānōs ōdit et Trōiam dēlēre cupit. Minerva Trōiānōs dē perīculō monērī nōn cupit. Itaque serpentēs magnās in terram mittit. Serpentēs ācrēs Lāocoontem et filiōs occīdunt.

_____

_____

_____

_____

_____

_____

_____

_____

_____

_____

_____

ante + *acc.* – before	**ōdit** – (s)/he hates
Lāocoōn, Lāocoontis, *m.* – Laocoön, a Trojan priest	**porta, portae,** *f.* – gate
ligneus, lignea, ligneum – wooden	**positus, posita, positum** – positioned, placed
Minerva, Minervae, *f.* – Minerva (Athena)	**serpēns, serpentis,** *f.* – serpent
mittō, mittere, mīsī, missum – to send	**Trōia, Trōiae,** *f.* – Troy
moneō, monēre, monuī, monitum – to warn	**Trōiānus, Trōiāna, Trōiānum** – Trojan
occīdō, occīdere, occīdī, occīsum – to kill	**Trōiānus, Trōiānī,** *m.* – Trojan

▶ EXERCISE 7

Translate into Latin.

1. The fortunate are able to flee. _____

2. I do not believe that the Trojans are fortunate. _____
   Trōiānus, Trōiānī, *m.*

3. Flames are destroying Troy. _____
   Trōia, Trōiae, *f.*

4. War is not feared by the Trojans. _____

5. The danger is not understood by the Trojans. _____

6. Many want to flee. _____

7. Not a few Trojans are captured by the enemies. _____

CONTENT QUESTIONS

After completing Chapter 10, answer these questions.

1. Which present forms of the third conjugation–*iō* verbs resemble the fourth conjugation?

   _____

2. Where does the main difference between third declension adjectives of one, two, and three endings appear?

   _____

3. What group of third declension nouns do the third declension adjectives resemble?

   _____

   _____

4. What famous epic poem deals with the mythical origins of Rome?

   _____

5. From what eastern race did the Romans believe they had descended?

   _____

6. Which Greek devised the plan of the wooden horse that brought about the fall of Troy?

   _____

Ruins of the walls from one of the levels of the ancient city of Troy.

CHAPTER 11

▶ EXERCISE 1

Conjugate the following verbs in the imperfect active and passive voice. Write an English translation for each form.

1. *firmō, firmāre, firmāvī, firmātum*

Imperfect Active: *firmō*

	Singular	Plural
First person	_____ _____	_____ _____
Second person	_____ _____	_____ _____
Third person	_____ _____	_____ _____

Imperfect Passive: *firmō*

	Singular	Plural
First person	_____ _____	_____ _____
Second person	_____ _____	_____ _____
Third person	_____ _____	_____ _____

2. *mittō, mittere, mīsī, missum*

Imperfect Active: *mittō*

	Singular	Plural
First person	_____ _____	_____ _____
Second person	_____ _____	_____ _____
Third person	_____ _____	_____ _____

Imperfect Passive: *mittō*

	Singular	Plural
First person	_____ _____	_____ _____
Second person	_____ _____	_____ _____
Third person	_____ _____	_____ _____

▶ EXERCISE 2

Match the meaning of the Latin word in Column B to the English derivative in Column A. Some meanings may be used more than once, others not at all.

Column A	Column B
1. _____ crude	A. storm
2. _____ actress	B. leave behind
3. _____ relic	C. together
4. _____ tempest	D. grief
5. _____ ardent	E. burn
6. _____ omit	F. cruel
7. _____ vicereine	G. also
8. _____ spelunker	H. new
9. _____ Delores	I. forest
10. _____ conspicuous	J. queen
11. _____ novice	K. least
12. _____ savage	L. cave
13. _____ demise	M. send
14. _____ innovation	N. drive, do
15. _____ promise	O. observe
16. _____ novel	
17. _____ agenda	
18. _____ missionary	
19. _____ Dolly	
20. _____ reliquary	

▶ EXERCISE 3

Translate into English.

1. Timēbāris. _____

2. Movēbāminī. _____

3. Multa sentiēbant. _____

4. Manēbāmus iacēbāmusque. _____

5. Audīrī quoque poterāmus. _____

6. Praeclāra fortisque vidēbātur. _____

7. Crūdēlēs nōn erant. _____

8. Relinquēbārisne . . . ? _____

9. Nōn erant miserī sed fēlīcēs. _____

10. Manēre ūnā poterātis. _____

▶ EXERCISE 4

Translate into Latin.

1. I was conquering. _____

2. It was being told. _____

3. You (plural) were able to be freed. _____

4. You were being seen. _____

5. They were burning. _____

6. They were brave. _____

7. You were able to come. _____

8. You (plural) were accustomed to know. _____

9. You (plural) were being called. _____

10. We were being called. _____

▶ EXERCISE 5

Fill in the blanks using the verb in parentheses and translate each sentence. The Reading Vocabulary in Chapter 11 may be consulted for names.

Example: Dīdō sē esse rēgīnam fēlīcem ___putābat___. (*was thinking*)
Dido was thinking that she was a fortunate queen.

1. Amor Dīdōnis et Aenēae _____ magnus. (*was*)

   _____

2. Aenēās et Dīdō ad spēluncam _____. (*were walking*)

   _____

3. Aenēās et Dīdō in silvā _____. (*were*)

4. Tempestās ab Aenēā Dīdōneque _____. (*was not being observed*)

_____

5. Cīvēs Aenēam cupere terram novam petere _____. (*did not believe*)

_____

6. Aenēās contrā deōs pugnāre _____. (*was not able*)

_____

Dido and Aeneas as depicted on a seventeenth-century tapestry.

▶ EXERCISE 6

Translate the following passage into Latin.

Aeneas and Dido were wanting to stay together. They seemed to be fortunate to the citizens. Aeneas was not thinking about the words of the gods. The king of the gods understood that Aeneas could not remain with Dido. Dido was unable to overcome the gods, but she grieved greatly. Dido's spirit could not be strengthened. Death seemed to be good to Dido.

_____

_____

_____

_____

_____

_____

_____

Aenēās (*acc.* **Aenēam**), *m.* – Aeneas
Dīdō, Dīdōnis, *f.* – Dido

Dido on a wall painting from Pompeii.

▶ EXERCISE 7

Choose the best answer for the following questions and translate. The Latin reading passage in Chapter 11 should be consulted for an accurate response.

1. Eratne Dīdō rēgīna?

    Dīdō rēgīna amōre ārdēbat.

    Dīdō erat rēgīna.

    Dīdō Aenēam valdē amābat.

    _____

    _____

2. Veniēbatne tempestās magna?

    Tempestās cōnspiciēbātur.

    Aenēās et Dīdō tempestātem timēbant.

    Tempestās magna veniēbat.

    _____

    _____

3. Cūr (why) Aenēās et Dīdō in spēluncā manēbant?

    Aenēās et Dīdō in silvā erant.

    Aenēās et Dīdō in silvā ambulābant.

    Aenēās et Dīdō in tempestāte esse nōn cupiēbant.

    _____

    _____

4. Intellegēbatne Aenēās sē ā Dīdōne amārī?

    Aenēās amōrem Dīdōnis vidēbat.

    Aenēās Dīdōnem amābat.

    Aenēās sē Dīdōnem amāre dīcēbat.

_____

_____

5. Cūr (*why*) Aenēās Dīdōque erant fēlīcēs?

    Aenēās et Dīdō saepe ūnā cōnspiciēbantur.

    Aenēās dē deōrum verbīs nōn cōgitābat.

    Aenēās Dīdōque propter amōrem gaudium sentiēbant.

_____

_____

6. Cūr (*why*) Aenēās Dīdōnem relinquere dēbēbat?

    Aenēās urbem Dīdōnis timēbat.

    Aenēās dē Mercuriī verbīs cōgitābat.

    Aenēās dē terrā novā cōgitābat.

_____

_____

CONTENT QUESTIONS

After completing Chapter 11, answer these questions.

1. In what city was Aeneas welcomed at the court of Dido?

_____

2. What syllable is the sign of the imperfect tense in all of the conjugations?

_____

3. What is the meaning of the imperfect tense?

_____

4. What other verb do the endings of the imperfect tense of *possum* resemble?

_____

5. What is an enclitic?

_____

6. What do the enclitics –*que* and –*ne* mean?

_____

_____

CHAPTER 12

▶ EXERCISE 1

Decline the following phrases.

1. *nōmen meum*

	Singular	**Plural**
Nominative	_____	_____
Genitive	_____	_____
Dative	_____	_____
Accusative	_____	_____
Ablative	_____	_____

2. *ignis tuus*

	Singular	**Plural**
Nominative	_____	_____
Genitive	_____	_____
Dative	_____	_____
Accusative	_____	_____
Ablative	_____	_____

3. *īra nostra*

	Singular	**Plural**
Nominative	_____	_____
Genitive	_____	_____
Dative	_____	_____
Accusative	_____	_____
Ablative	_____	_____

4. *vīs vestra*

	Singular	**Plural**
Nominative	_____	_____
Genitive	_____	_____
Dative	_____	_____
Accusative	_____	_____
Ablative	_____	_____

▶ EXERCISE 2

Complete the sentence, fill in the blank, or answer the question, all based on derivation.

1. Which of the following rocks are of volcanic origin?

    a. auriferous

    b. igneous

    c. arenicolous

    d. ferrous

2. People who use their left hands as well as they do their right are called _____.

    a. ambidextrous

    b. ambivalent

    c. ambitious

    d. ambiguous

3. An **irascible** person

    a. makes a lot of mistakes.

    b. has a good sense of humor.

    c. loves bright colors.

    d. is often angry.

4. The word "renown" is derived from the Latin word meaning _____.

    a. fame

    b. to know

    c. name

    d. to feel

5. From which Latin word is "violate" derived?

    a. *vīta*

    b. *vīs*

    c. *vincō*

    d. *via*

6. The **nostrum** discussed at the gathering is a pet theory that _____ developed to solve all political problems.

    a. you

    b. they

    c. we

    d. I

7. The word "assembly" is derived from the same Latin root as _____.

    a. facsimile

    b. simian

    c. fascinate

    d. seminary

8. Which word is derived from the Latin root meaning "so great"?

    a. tantalize

    b. tantara

    c. tantrum

    d. tantamount

9. Which word is **NOT** derived from the same Latin root as the others?

    a. consumer

    b. sumac

    c. sumptuous

    d. presume

10. The verb *faciō* has countless derivatives. Which of the following is **NOT** one of them?

    a. forgery   b. petrify

    c. forfeiture   d. pacifism

11. Which word is derived from the same Latin root as "homicide"?

    a. incidental   b. parachute

    c. chisel   d. occident

12. The **apparent** reason for an action may not always be the real one.

    a. osteopathic   b. positive

    c. popular   d. ostensible

13. The system of **placing** riders and horses in relays along a road for speedy travel is the source for the word _____.

    a. postage   b. posture

    c. postpone   d. postulant

14. Which word is **NOT** derived from the Latin word meaning "near"?

    a. propinquity   b. appropriate

    c. proximity   d. approach

15. Once again all of the following derive from *faciō* **EXCEPT**

    a. chauffeur   b. soporific

    c. benefactor   d. fiscal

▶ EXERCISE 3

Translate into English.

1. Casa ab eō aedificātur. _____

2. Rēx meās fīliās nōn videt. _____

3. Mulier tibi similis est. _____

4. Fortitūdine tuā docēmur. _____

5. Flammārum vim nōn timeō. _____

6. Vōs nōn timeō. _____

7. Animum meum prō vīribus firmō. _____

▶ EXERCISE 4

Translate into Latin.

1. to/for my pain   _____

2. of your word   _____

3. your (plural) friends   _____

4. by/with my sister   _____

5. of your (plural) gifts _____

6. It was being observed by our son. _____

7. I think about your prize. _____

8. My daughters are loved by me. _____

▶ EXERCISE 5

Supply the correct corresponding form of *is, ea, id* in the following phrases.

1. those things   _____

2. by/with that woman   _____

3. of those people   _____

4. of those women   _____

5. of those things   _____

6. by/with these people _____

7. his   _____

8. hers   _____

9. to him   _____

10. to her   _____

11. to it   _____

12. she   _____

13. by/with this man   _____

14. by/with that thing   _____

Mucius Scaevola places his hand in the fire in front
of the king of the Etruscans.

▶ EXERCISE 6

Translate the following passage into English.

Mūcius erat cīvis Rōmānus et homō fortis. In Etrūscōrum castra intrat. Rēgem Etrūscōrum occīdere cupit, nec eius mīlitēs timet. Sed hostium vīrēs nōn intellegit. Itaque Mūcius ab hostibus capitur. Rēx Etrūscōrum Mūcium ad sē vocat. "Tū es mihi hostis," inquit, "et hostium meōrum nōmina mihi dīcere dēbēs." Ignēs prope Mūcium ā mīlitibus Etrūscīs pōnuntur. Mūcius autem nec ignēs nec rēgis īram timet. "Vī," inquit Mūcius, "mē vincere nōn potes."

_____

_____

_____

_____

_____

_____

_____

_____

_____

_____

nec ... nec ... – neither ... nor ...

▶ EXERCISE 7

Choose the best answer for the following questions and translate. The Latin reading passage in Chapter 12 should be consulted for an accurate response.

1. Rēgemne Etrūscōrum timēbat Mūcius?

    Etrūscī semper timēbant.

    Rōmānī hostēs timēbant.

    Mūcius rēgem nōn timēbat.

    _____

    _____

2. Cupiēbatne Mūcius rēgem Etrūscōrum servāre?

    Mūcius fortitūdinem ostendere cupiēbat.

    Mūcius rēgem hostium occīdere cupiēbat.

    Mūcius in Etrūscōrum castra intrāre cupiēbat.

    _____

    _____

3. Suntne Rōmānī Mūciō similēs?

    Rōmānī sunt multī Mūciō similēs.

    Rōmānī rēgem Etrūscōrum timent.

    Rōmānī sunt Etrūscīs similēs.

    _____

    _____

4. Dēbēbatne rēx Etrūscōrum cīvēs Rōmānōs semper timēre?

    Rēx Etrūscōrum cīvēs Rōmānōs semper timēre nōn dēbēbat.

    Rēx Etrūscōrum hostēs semper timēre dēbēbat.

    Rēx Etrūscōrum īrā semper movētur.

    _____

    _____

5. Dēbēbatne rēx Etrūscōrum hostēs domī timēre?

    Rēx Etrūscōrum hostēs occīdere cupiēbat.

    Rēx Etrūscōrum perīculum timēre nōn dēbēbat.

    Rēx Etrūscōrum hostēs in castrīs et domī timēre dēbēbat.

    _____

    _____

6. Dīcitne rēx Etrūscōrum Mūciō ex ignibus esse perīculum?

     Rēx Etrūscōrum flammās semper timēbat.

     Rēx Etrūscōrum dīcit Mūcium ignēs timēre dēbēre.

     Dīcit rēx Etrūscōrum Mūcium ē castrīs fugere dēbēre.

_____

_____

7. Crēdēbatne rēx Mūciī fortitūdinem vincī posse?

     Crēdēbat rēx sē hostēs fortēs vincere posse.

     Intellegit rēx sē Mūcium vincere nōn posse.

     Rēx Rōmānōs nōn esse fortēs putat.

_____

_____

Etruscan soldier's breastplate.

CONTENT QUESTIONS

After completing Chapter 12, answer these questions.

1. Why is the noun *vīs* called defective?

    _____

2. The demonstrative *is, ea, id* has forms that you have already seen in declensions of nouns. In which declensions can we find forms parallel to those of *is, ea, id*?

    _____

3. What case endings of *is, ea, id* are not paralleled in any of the declensions you have seen so far?

    _____

4. What did the Roman historian Livy apparently believe about the Roman morals of his own day?

    _____

5. With which Roman emperor did Livy have connections?

    _____

6. What was the title of Livy's work, and what does it mean?

    _____

CHAPTER 13

▶ EXERCISE 1

Give the positive and negative imperatives of the following verbs.

	Positive Imperative		Negative Imperative	
	Singular	Plural	Singular	Plural
1. *intrō, intrāre, intrāvī, intrātum*	_____	_____	_____	_____
2. *doceō, docēre, docuī, doctum*	_____	_____	_____	_____
3. *mittō, mittere, mīsī, missum*	_____	_____	_____	_____
4. *fugiō, fugere, fūgī, ——*	_____	_____	_____	_____
5. *veniō, venīre, vēnī, ventum*	_____	_____	_____	_____

▶ EXERCISE 2

Complete the sentence, fill in the blank, or answer the question, all based on derivation.

1. What is the meaning of the Latin word from which we derive "annihilate"?

   a. destroy

   c. nothing

   b. now

   d. new

2. Which response is derived from the Latin word *suus*?

   a. suit

   c. suite

   b. suicide

   d. suitor

3. Which of the following describes a "quidnunc"?

   a. Marcella, who is often bored

   c. Federico, who is a baseball announcer

   b. Luigi, who can't figure out a math problem

   d. Venus, who loves to hear the latest gossip

4. Which word is **NOT** derived from the same Latin root?

   a. judicature

   c. adjunct

   b. injudicious

   d. prejudice

5. What is the meaning of the Latin word from which we derive "alien"?

   a. other

   c. allow

   b. foreign

   d. free

6. The "Dives" in the parable recorded by Luke (16:19–31) is the _____ man.
   a. wounded
   b. rich
   c. holy
   d. giving

7. A **docile** child
   a. lives at home.
   b. is kind and generous.
   c. leads his friends into mischief.
   d. is easily taught.

8. Which of the following are "omnivorous"?
   a. fish
   b. cows
   c. butterflies
   d. humans

9. What is the **SYNONYM** of "omnipresent"?
   a. ubiquitous
   b. immortal
   c. sempiternal
   d. temporary

10. Which of the following is **NOT** derived from the root of *discēdō*?
    a. deceased
    b. success
    c. reception
    d. ancestor

11. The Latin verb meaning "to lead" is the root of all the following **EXCEPT**
    a. induce
    b. dubious
    c. redoubt
    d. viaduct

12. Which of the following is **NOT** derived from *licet*?
    a. illicit
    b. leisure
    c. license
    d. relic

13. Choose the **ANTONYM** of *nōlō*.
    a. *vocō*
    b. *voleō*
    c. *volō*
    d. *volvō*

14. Which of the following is **NOT** derived from the same Latin root as "respond"?
    a. spontaneity
    b. correspond
    c. irresponsible
    d. despondent

15. A person who **asks** for undeserved rights
    a. is a bad leader.
    b. is arrogant.
    c. answers to no one.
    d. exhibits illegal behavior.

16. The **departing** president gave a(n) _____.

    a. valediction   b. introduction

    c. derogation   d. salutation

17. Which of the following is **NOT** derived from the preposition *prō*?

    a. providence   b. progression

    c. proposition   d. protocol

▶ EXERCISE 3

Change the positive or negative singular imperatives into the plural and the plural forms into the singular. Translate the changed forms.

Example: nāvigāte!
nāvigā!   sail!

1. vidē!   _____

2. mitte!   _____

3. ostende!   _____

4. habitāte!   _____

5. audī!   _____

6. nōlī iubēre!   _____

7. cōnspice!   _____

8. dēlē!   _____

9. cupite!   _____

10. nōlīte dolēre! _____

11. nārrā!   _____

▶ EXERCISE 4

Fill in the blanks either with a form of *suus, sua, suum* or with *eius, eōrum, eārum* and translate the sentences.

Example: Vir dē cōnsiliō _____suō_____ cōgitat.
The man thinks of/about his plan.

1. Rōmānī contrā hostēs pugnant et _____ urbem dēlent.

    _____

2. Dīvitēs praemia _____ servāre cupiunt.

    _____

3. Agricola terram _____ cūrat, āthlēta corpus suum.

    _____

4. Poēta virum audiēbat et _____ verba nōn amābat.

_____

5. Doctī librōs _____ semper tenent.

_____

6. Ducēs mīlitēs _____ dūcunt.

_____

▶ EXERCISE 5

Translate into Latin. (Some are Horace's own thoughts.)

1. The poet builds his monument.
   monumentum, monumentī, *n.* – monument

_____

2. The poet builds a monument and the monument can remain forever.

_____

3. Not all parts of me have to die.
   pars, partis, *f.* – part   **morī** – to die

_____

4. Not all parts of us must die.

_____

5. Who of you (plural) does not desire to live always?
   quis? – who?

_____

6. I say these words because of love for/of you.

_____

A Roman shield such as the one that Horace says he threw down in battle.

▶ EXERCISE 6

Translate into English the following anecdote related to an event in Horace's life.

Horātius erat mīles et in bellō pugnāre dēbēbat. Is tamen cōgitābat: "Multī nostrum in bellō occīduntur. Ducēs nōs pugnāre iubent, sed verba eōrum audīre nōn dēbēmus. Ūnusquisque nostrum corpus suum servāre potest. Bonum et pulchrum est prō patriā morī, sed propter amōrem meī vītam meam habēre cupiō." Tunc poēta scūtum suum relinquit et fugit.

_____

_____

_____

_____

_____

_____

_____

_____

Horātius, Horātiī, _m._ – Horace   **scūtum, scūtī,** _n._ – shield
morī – to die   **ūnusquisque** – each one

Horace wrote in *Satire* 1.9 that he was walking along the *Via Sacra* in the Roman Forum. The *Via Sacra* runs on a slight diagonal in this picture—from the grove of trees in the upper right corner into the Forum at the left.

▶ EXERCISE 7

For each question, choose the best answer and translate. Refer to the Latin reading passage in Chapter 13, if necessary.

1. Ubi (*where*) erat Horātius?

    Horātius in sacrō templō erat.

    Horātius in agrīs erat.

    Horātius in viā erat.

    Horātius in spēluncā erat.

    _____

    _____

2. Quid cupiēbat importūnus?

    Poētae importūnus verba dīcere cupiēbat.

    Importūnus pugnāre cupiēbat.

    Importūnus ambulāre nōn cupiēbat.

    Importūnus cōnsilia capere cupiēbat.

    _____

    _____

3. Quid cupiēbat Horātius?

    Horātius verba dīcere cupiēbat.

    Horātius nihil cūrābat.

    Horātius fugere cupiēbat.

    Horātius ōrātiōnem habēre cupiēbat.

    _____

    _____

4. Quid Horātius dē Maecēnāte dīcēbat?

    Horātius Maecēnātem nōn amābat.

    Horātius ā Maecēnāte fugere cupiēbat.

    Horātius nihil dē Maecēnāte sciēbat.

    Horātius dē Maecēnātis domō bona verba dīcēbat.

    _____

    _____

5. Quōmodo (*how*) Horātius servātur?

    Alius homō importūnum ad iūdicem vocat.

    Importūnus ad casam fugit.

    Iūdex importūnum līberat.

    Horātius importūnum discēdere iubet.

    _____

    _____

CONTENT QUESTIONS

After completing Chapter 13, answer these questions.

1. What does the grammatical term "mood" mean?

    _____

    _____

2. Which moods of the verb do you know by now?

    _____

3. What words are used to form the negative imperative?

    _____

4. Who was Maecenas?

    _____

5. What was Horace's ideal in life?

    _____

6. What characterizes the literature of Augustan times?

    _____

CHAPTER 14

▶ EXERCISE 1

Conjugate the following verbs in the future active and passive, singular and plural. Write an English translation for each form.

1. *līberō, līberāre, līberāvī, līberātum*

Future Active: *līberō*

	Singular		Plural	
First person	_____	_____	_____	_____
Second person	_____	_____	_____	_____
Third person	_____	_____	_____	_____

Future Passive: *līberō*

	Singular		Plural	
First person	_____	_____	_____	_____
Second person	_____	_____	_____	_____
Third person	_____	_____	_____	_____

2. *iubeō, iubēre, iussī, iussum*

Future Active: *iubeō*

	Singular		Plural	
First person	_____	_____	_____	_____
Second person	_____	_____	_____	_____
Third person	_____	_____	_____	_____

Future Passive: *iubeō*

	Singular		Plural	
First person	_____	_____	_____	_____
Second person	_____	_____	_____	_____
Third person	_____	_____	_____	_____

▶ EXERCISE 2

Complete the sentence, fill in the blank, or answer the question, all based on derivation.

1. Which of the following are **arboreal** creatures?

   a. dogs

   b. giraffes

   c. monkeys

   d. zebras

2. Which flower has leaves shaped like **swords**?

   a. gladiolus

   b. rose

   c. iris

   d. azalea

3. Pink eyes, light hair, and pale, milky skin are all characteristics of a(n) _____.

   a. alcoholic

   b. Scotsman

   c. Scandinavian

   d. albino

4. The **pectoral** muscles are located in the _____.

   a. arm

   b. chest

   c. leg

   d. back

5. Which of the following is **NOT** derived from *odium*?

   a. odious

   b. annoy

   c. ennui

   d. odorous

6. Which of the following is **NOT** derived from the Latin word meaning "mouth"?

   a. ossify

   b. orifice

   c. usher

   d. oral

7. Which of the following is derived from the same Latin root as "parent"?

   a. apparent

   b. imperial

   c. compare

   d. repertoire

8. Peter and Paul were related by **consanguinity**.

   a. Their wives were sisters.

   b. They were brothers.

   c. They lived next door to each other.

   d. They had been playmates since childhood.

9. Sangria is a drink that is _____ in color.

   a. blue

   b. green

   c. orange

   d. red

10. The student's **sanguine** complexion gave evidence of her _____.

   a. confidence

   b. worry

   c. anger

   d. disappointment

11. The **sanguinary** battle was

    a. easily won.

    b. fought to a draw.

    c. long and bloody.

    d. filled with heroic acts.

12. Choose the **ANTONYM** of **primal**.

    a. basic

    b. prehistoric

    c. aboriginal

    d. subordinate

13. Which of the following is **NOT** derived from *ruber*?

    a. rouge

    b. rough

    c. rubric

    d. ruby

14. Which of the following is **NOT** derived from *cadō*?

    a. deciduous

    b. cascade

    c. suicide

    d. cadence

15. The word "obese" is derived from the Latin root meaning _____.

    a. to eat

    b. to grow

    c. to burden

    d. to be

16. The word "convention" is derived from the same Latin root as _____.

    a. souvenir

    b. ventriloquist

    c. ventilation

    d. sovereign

17. The **confluent** rivers

    a. were at flood stage.

    b. were equal in length.

    c. flowed together.

    d. ran swiftly.

18. The word "separate" is derived from the Latin words meaning "self" and _____.

    a. part

    b. small

    c. equal

    d. obtain

19. The tactile senses are located in the _____.

    a. eyes

    b. fingers

    c. ears

    d. mouth

20. Which of the following is **NOT** derived from *tangō*?

    a. intact

    b. integration

    c. tactful

    d. taciturn

21. Which of the following is **NOT** derived from the preposition *per*?

    a. persimmon   b. person

    c. perspective   d. permit

▶ EXERCISE 3

Identify the case, number, and gender of the following forms of the relative pronoun. Give all possible answers.

Example: quae
feminine singular nominative   feminine plural nominative   neuter plural nominative
neuter plural accusative

1. quō   _____

2. quī   _____

3. cūius   _____

4. quā   _____

5. cui   _____

6. quōrum   _____

7. quibus   _____

8. quod   _____

9. quam   _____

10. quem   _____

▶ EXERCISE 4

Change the singular forms into plural and the plural into singular. Translate the changed form.

Example: ārdēbis
ārdēbitis   you (plural) will burn

1. cōgitābit   _____

2. firmābiminī   _____

3. iūdicābis   _____

4. dolēbimus   _____

5. docēbunt   _____

6. manēbō   _____

7. poteris   _____

8. poterunt   _____

9. erit   _____

10. līberāberis   _____

11. rogābitur   _____

▶ EXERCISE 5

Change the forms in the active voice into passive and the passive forms into the active voice. Translate the changed form.

Example: habēbiminī
habēbitis   you (plural) will have

1. dēlēbuntur   _____

2. dabit   _____

3. vocābimus   _____

4. docēbis   _____

5. iubēbiminī   _____

6. putābō   _____

7. servābunt   _____

8. sēparāberis   _____

9. docēbor   _____

10. nārrābimur   _____

11. amābitur   _____

▶ EXERCISE 6

Choose which one of the four statements is true based on the Latin reading passage in Chapter 14 and translate the statement. The Reading Vocabulary may be consulted.

1. Parentēs Pȳramī Thisbēn amant.

    Parentēs Thisbēs Pȳramum amant.

    Puer ā puellā, quam amat, pariete sēparātur.

    Inter Pȳramum et Thisbēn est odium.

    _____

    _____

2. Pȳramus Thisbēn tenēbit.

    Pȳramus Thisbēn nōn vidēbit.

    Pȳramus leaenam vidēbit.

    Pȳramus erit in spēluncā.

    _____

    _____

3. Pȳramus et Thisbē convenīre dēbent prope arborem, in quā sunt pōma rubra.

In arbore sunt pōma alba et pōma rubra.

Pōma, quae erant alba, mox erunt rubra.

Pōma, quae erant rubra, mox erunt alba.

_____

_____

4. Pȳramus, quī leaenam timet, fugit.

Pȳramus et Thisbē ā leaenā fugiunt.

Thisbē leaenam nōn videt.

Thisbē, quae leaenam videt, fugit.

_____

_____

5. Pȳramus iam nōn cupit vīvere.

Leaena Pȳramum comedit.

Leaena Thisbēn comedit.

Pȳramus leaenam occīdit.

_____

_____

6. Thisbē sē occīdit.

Leaena Thisbēn comedit.

Thisbē Pȳramum gladiō occīdit.

Thisbē Pȳramō gladium dat.

_____

_____

Thisbe stands next to the wall that separates
her from Pyramus.

▶ EXERCISE 7

Fill in the blanks with the correct case, number, and gender of the relative pronoun and translate the sentences. The Reading Vocabulary may be consulted.

Example: Thisbē, _____quae_____ prope Pȳramum habitābat, ab eō amābātur.
Thisbe, who lived close to Pyramus, was beloved by him.

1. Pȳramus et Thisbē nōn amābant parietem, _____ sēparābantur.

   _____

2. Pariēs, _____ Pȳramus et Thisbē verba dīcēbant, nōn respondēbat.

   _____

3. Leaena appropinquābit ad puellam, _____ exspectābit.

   _____

4. Vēlāmen, _____ puella habēbat, in terram cadit.

   _____

5. Thisbē sē occīdit gladiō, _____ Pȳramus sē occīdit.

   _____

A profile of Publius Ovidius Nāso, author of the *Metamorphōsēs*.

CONTENT QUESTIONS

After completing Chapter 14, answer these questions.

1. What does the title *Metamorphōsēs* mean, whose work is it, and why is it called by this name?

   ____

   ____

2. Name an important event in Ovid's life.

   ____

   ____

3. How do you form the future indicative of the first and the second conjugation?

   ____

   ____

4. Which noun declensions do the forms of the relative pronoun resemble?

   ____

   ____

5. What is an antecedent?

   ____

   ____

6. What determines the case, number, and gender of the relative pronoun?

   ____

   ____

CHAPTER 15

▶ EXERCISE 1

Conjugate the following verbs in the future active and passive, singular and plural. Write an English translation for each form.

1. *relinquō, relinquere, relīquī, relictum*

Future Active: *relinquō*

	Singular		**Plural**	
First person	_____	_____	_____	_____
Second person	_____	_____	_____	_____
Third person	_____	_____	_____	_____

Future Passive: *relinquō*

	Singular		**Plural**	
First person	_____	_____	_____	_____
Second person	_____	_____	_____	_____
Third person	_____	_____	_____	_____

2. *sciō, scīre, scīvī, scītum*

Future Active: *sciō*

	Singular		**Plural**	
First person	_____	_____	_____	_____
Second person	_____	_____	_____	_____
Third person	_____	_____	_____	_____

Future Passive: *sciō*

	Singular		**Plural**	
First person	_____	_____	_____	_____
Second person	_____	_____	_____	_____
Third person	_____	_____	_____	_____

▶ EXERCISE 2

Complete the sentence, fill in the blank, or answer the question, all based on derivation.

1. A **saxifrage** is a plant that grows
   a. during the winter
   b. in the clefts of rocks
   c. as an epiphyte on trees
   d. at the bottom of the sea

2. The word "seniority" is derived from the Latin root meaning
   a. above
   b. sit
   c. old
   d. follow

3. Which of the following is derived from *vīlla*?
   a. villain
   b. villus
   c. villosity
   d. villous

4. Which of the following is derived from the same Latin root as "difficult"?
   a. difference
   b. diffident
   c. defend
   d. defeat

5. Which of the following is derived from *parvus*?
   a. parvenu
   b. partitive
   c. paraffin
   d. paring

6. Choose the **ANTONYM** of "rural."
   a. villain
   b. urban
   c. provincial
   d. maritime

7. The adverb "very" is derived from the Latin word meaning _____.
   a. come
   b. word
   c. old
   d. true

8. Which of the following is derived from the Latin root meaning "old"?
   a. veteran
   b. veto
   c. vibrate
   d. viburnum

9. Which of the following does **NOT** belong by derivation?
   a. negligee
   b. negligence
   c. negative
   d. neglect

10. A "statue" is so-called because it _____.
    a. exists
    b. stands still
    c. is interesting
    d. is preserved

11. All of the following derive from *stō* **EXCEPT**

    a. superstition

    b. extant

    c. existence

    d. stolid

12. "Ubiquity" is the capability to be

    a. knowledgeable in everything.

    b. all things to all people.

    c. everywhere at the same time.

    d. a lover of all horses.

13. Which of the following does **NOT** derive from the Latin word *ante*?

    a. anticlimax

    b. antiquarian

    c. antics

    d. anterior

▶ EXERCISE 3
Translate into Latin.

1. Whose country house is neglected?

    _____

2. What country house is neglected?

    _____

3. Which country houses are neglected?

    _____

4. Whose (plural) country houses are neglected?

    _____

5. To whom is the country house being given?

    _____

6. To whom (plural) are the country houses being given?

    _____

7. By what man is the country house being given to me?

    _____

8. By what woman is the country house being given to me?

    _____

9. By which people is the country house being given to me?

    _____

10. What country house do we see?

    _____

11. Which country houses do we see?

    _____

12. From which country houses are they coming?

_____

13. Who is living in the country house?

_____

14. Who are living in the country house?

_____

15. With what man were you fleeing?

_____

16. With what woman will you flee?

_____

▶ EXERCISE 4

Change the verbs in the imperfect tense into the future, keeping the same person, number, and voice. Translate the changed forms.

Example: ostendēbantur
ostendentur   they will be shown

1. cōnspiciēbāminī _____

2. fugiēbant _____

3. pōnēbātis _____

4. capiēbāmur _____

5. mittēbāris _____

6. vincēbāmur _____

7. neglegēbat _____

8. petēbāris _____

9. tangēbam _____

▶ EXERCISE 5

Translate into Latin.

1. An indication of old age.

   _____

2. The stones of my villa.

   _____

3. The small country houses.

   _____

4. Which rural roads?

   _____

5. About the trees which we see.

   _____

6. Which (things) are true?

   _____

7. Look here! The country house of Seneca!

   _____

8. Do not, friends, look at the old man who is standing by the country house.

   _____

Seneca, first the tutor and later the advisor to the emperor Nero, was accused of conspiracy
and was asked to slit his wrists. When he did not die quickly enough, he is said to have
settled into a tub of warm water in order to make the blood flow faster.

▶ EXERCISE 6

Translate the following passage into Latin. Use the Vocabulary to Learn in Chapter 15 and the words listed
below the passage.

I shall come to my country house, and there will be joy for me. I always said and I always shall say that I love
the rural life. However, I always had to live in the city because of official duties. But now there is leisure for
me. So I shall flee from the city and I shall seek my rural land. I shall leave the civic life. I shall remain in my
country house and I shall live there. What will I do there? What friends will I have? The farmers will be <my>
friends, with whom I shall take care of the trees. There will be fields there, which I shall observe with joy.

_____

_____

_____

_____

_____

_____

_____

cīvīlis, cīvīle – civic, official, public

officium, officiī, *n.* – duty

ōtium, ōtiī, *n.* – leisure

The Villa of Diomedes lies outside Pompeii on the south side of the Roman road, today called the Via dei Sepolcri, that led to Herculaneum. The villa sits beyond the last group of tombs on the left of the road and opposite the tomb of Marcus Arrius Diomedes, for whom the villa is named. The large villa is known for its fresco series and for its grand size and scale including a set of private baths.

▶ EXERCISE 7

Choose which one of the three statements is true based on the Latin reading passage in Chapter 15 and translate the statement. The Reading Vocabulary may be consulted.

1. Senectūtem timēre dēbēmus.

   Contrā senectūtem pugnāre nōn dēbēmus.

   Vīlla ā Senecā neglegitur.

   _____

   _____

2. Senex, quī ante Senecam stat, senectūtem nōn amat.

   Difficile Senecae est senem, quī prope vīllam stat, vidēre.

   Seneca cum homine, quī prope vīllam stat, quondam lūdēbat puer.

   _____

   _____

3. Senex, quī prope vīllam stat, Senecam spectat.

   Iānua, prope quam stat senex, ā Senecā nōn cōgnōscitur.

   Arborēs sunt prope iānuam.

   _____

   _____

4. Vīlla Senecae vidēbātur dē senectūte dīcere.

   Vīlla Senecae vidēbātur senectūtem exspectāre.

   Vīlla Senecae vidēbātur saxa nōn habēre.

   _____

   _____

5. Seneca dīcit arborēs prope vīllam cadere.

   Seneca dīcit sē arborēs prope vīllam posuisse.

   Vīlicus dīcit sē arborēs prope vīllam posuisse.

   _____

   _____

6. Arborēs ā vīlicō nōn cūrābantur.

   Arborēs ā vīlicō nōn semper cūrābantur.

   Arborēs ā vīlicō cūrābantur.

   _____

   _____

The tomb of Lucius Annaeus Seneca,
built alongside the Via Appia.

▶ EXERCISE 8

In the following passage you are going to read about some habits of Roman senators. The passage is written from the point of view of a modern historian, so all the verbs are in the imperfect tense. Rewrite the passage changing all the verbs into the future tense. You can imagine that you are Romulus, the legendary founder of Rome, predicting the future habits of the senators of the state you have founded. Finally, translate the rewritten passage into English.

Senātōrēs Rōmānī nōn paucī nōn sōlum in urbe habitābant, sed etiam vīllās habēbant. In urbe multa faciēbant. Ibi enim officia cīvīlia cūrāre dēbēbant. Multī autem eōrum tumultum et perīcula urbis nōn amābant. Nam terram rūsticam amābant, in quā erat tranquillitās. Itaque vīllās saepe petere cupiēbant. Interdum urbem relinquēbant et diū in vīllīs manēbant, in quibus dē litterīs et dē philosophiā cōgitāre poterant. In terrā rūsticā sē vītam vēram habēre sentiēbant. Terram rūsticam esse patriam vēram crēdēbant.

_____

_____

_____

_____

_____

_____

_____

_____

_____

_____

_____

_____

_____

_____

_____

_____

_____

cīvīlis, cīvīle – civil, political
interdum (*adv.*) – sometimes
officium, officiī, *n.* – duty
philosophia, philosophiae, *f.* – philosophy

senātor, senātōris, *m.* – senator (derived from *senex,* since the Senate was a "council of elders")
tranquillitās, tranquillitātis, *f.* – peacefulness, tranquillity
tumultus, tumultūs, *m.* – uproar, disturbance

CONTENT QUESTIONS

After completing Chapter 15, answer these questions.

1. In what form did Seneca write his philosophical essays?

   _____

2. What public role did Seneca play in the time of Nero?

   _____

3. What are the vowels that appear in the endings of the future of the third and fourth conjugation?

   _____

4. The future tense forms of the third conjugation *–iō* verbs are identical to the future forms of what other conjugation?

   _____

5. Why is there no feminine form in the singular of the interrogative pronoun?

   _____

   _____

6. To what other form is the interrogative adjective identical?

   _____

CHAPTER 16

▶ EXERCISE 1

Conjugate the following verbs in the perfect active and translate each form.

1. *dēleō, dēlēre, dēlēvī, dēlētum*

Perfect Active: *dēleō*

Singular

First person   _____   _____

Second person   _____   _____

Third person   _____   _____

Plural

First person   _____   _____

Second person   _____   _____

Third person   _____   _____

2. *discēdō, discēdere, discessī, discessum*

Perfect Active: *discēdō*

Singular

First person   _____   _____

Second person   _____   _____

Third person   _____   _____

Plural

First person   _____   _____

Second person   _____   _____

Third person   _____   _____

3. *veniō, venīre, vēnī, ventum*

Perfect Active: *veniō*

Singular

First person   _____   _____

Second person   _____   _____

Third person   _____   _____

Plural

First person   _____   _____

Second person   _____   _____

Third person   _____   _____

▶ EXERCISE 2

Complete the sentence, fill in the blank, or answer the question, all based on derivation.

1. The **cerulean** color reminded me of _____.

    a. the seashore   b. the sky

    c. a cloud   d. a ruby

2. Which of the following does **NOT** belong by derivation?

    a. accusation   b. because

    c. excuse   d. caustic

3. Which of the following is my **avuncular** relative?

    a. uncle   b. nephew

    c. cousin   d. brother

4. What is the meaning of the Latin word from which "ceiling" is derived?

    a. head   b. to cover

    c. to fall   d. sky

5. What color is the down on the leaves of **cineraria**?

    a. rust   b. yellow

    c. gray   d. blue

6. Which of the following is derived from *cinis*?

    a. cinereous   b. cinch

    c. cinema   d. cinchona

7. Which of the following does **NOT** belong by derivation?

    a. classify   b. iconoclast

    c. classical   d. middle-class

8. The word "perfume" is derived from the Latin root meaning _____.

    a. scent   b. sweet

    c. skin   d. smoke

9. Which of the following does **NOT** belong by derivation?

    a. incendiary   b. frankincense

    c. censer   d. censorious

10. Which of the following describes someone who possesses **littoral** property?

    a. Max, who has a second home in the mountains

    b. Sye, who rents an apartment on Fifth Avenue

    c. Indra, who inherited a farm in Nebraska

    d. Philip, who spends a lot of time at his beach house

11. The word "matrix" is derived from the Latin word meaning _____.

    a. mother

    b. order

    c. middle

    d. origin

12. Which word does **NOT** belong by derivation?

    a. mountainous

    b. amount

    c. summon

    d. tantamount

13. The **naval** supplies were placed

    a. in a demilitarized zone.

    b. on a ship going to sea.

    c. in the intensive care unit of the hospital.

    d. in the produce department by the grocer.

14. Which of the following is derived from *pars*?

    a. separate

    b. parent

    c. compare

    d. repartee

15. All of the following are derived from *pars* **EXCEPT**

    a. parade

    b. party

    c. parcel

    d. participle

16. The house had a **funereal** atmosphere

    a. because of the recent fire.

    b. because it was empty.

    c. because its owner had recently died.

    d. because it was inhabited only by women.

17. Which of the following comes from the same Latin verb as "intelligence"?

    a. college

    b. legion

    c. illegal

    d. privilege

18. All of the following are derived from *legō, legere* **EXCEPT**

    a. cull

    b. lesson

    c. diligent

    d. relegate

19. Which of the following does **NOT** derive from the same Latin root as "oppression"?

    a. print

    b. surprise

    c. sprain

    d. reprimand

20. The word "etude" is derived from the Latin verb meaning _____.

    a. to study   b. to beat

    c. to give   d. to use

▶ EXERCISE 3

Translate into Latin.

1. They waited for the old man.   _____

2. He said nothing.   _____

3. We understood everything (all things).   _____

4. You did not send the letter.   _____

5. They saw the sea.   _____

6. You (plural) never answered.   _____

7. You ordered the soldier to speak.   _____

8. He left the shore.   _____

9. Stones fell from the mountain.   _____

10. The conflagration destroyed ships.   _____

A square-rigged Roman ship.

▶ EXERCISE 4

Change the imperfect active verbs into the corresponding perfect active, keeping the same person and number. Translate the changed form.

Example: sentiēbātis
sēnsistis   you (plural) felt *or* did feel *or* have felt

1. tangēbat   _____   _____
2. habitābāmus   _____   _____
3. agēbātis   _____   _____
4. dabam   _____   _____
5. docēbāmus   _____   _____
6. stābam   _____   _____
7. faciēbant   _____   _____
8. dēbēbās   _____   _____
9. dīcēbās   _____   _____

▶ EXERCISE 5

Fill in the blanks with the correct form of the perfect tense and translate the completed sentence.

Example: Nōs saxa et cinerēs in lītore vidēre ___potuimus___. (posse)
We were able to (could) see the stones and ashes on the shore.

1. Clādēs _____ magna et fūnesta. (esse)

    _____

2. Eō tempore multae nāvēs prope nōs _____. Posteā nihil vidēre _____. (esse, posse)

    _____

3. Ego epistulam tuam _____; tū autem meam numquam _____. (legere, legere)

    _____

4. Animōs fortēs habētis. Itaque ad hominēs, quī perīculum timent, nāvigāre _____. (dēcernere)

    _____

5. Saxum nōn _____. Itaque in terram _____. (cōnspicere, cadere)

    _____

6. Epistulam, quam nautae _____, nōn _____. (mittere, vidēre)

    _____

▶ EXERCISE 6

Change the following sentences so that they are constructed with the dative of possession. The object of each sentence will be the subject in the rewritten sentences. Then translate the rewritten sentences. The Reading Vocabulary in Chapter 16 may be consulted.

Example: Magnōs agrōs habeō.
Magnī mihi sunt agrī.   I have big fields.

1. Avunculus meus nāvēs habēbat.

   _____

   _____

2. Vīllam, quae est prope montem Vesuvium, habēmus.

   _____

   _____

3. Nōn habuī hostēs sed multōs amīcōs.

   _____

   _____

4. Nautae habent epistulam, quam fēmina, quae erat in lītore, mīsit.

   _____

   _____

5. Sum senex, sed corpus forte habeō.

   _____

   _____

6. Multās vīllās in vestrīs agrīs habētis.

   _____

   _____

The famous mosaic of a dog, found during the excavation of Pompeii, with the Latin words *Cavē Canem* or "Beware of the Dog."

▶ EXERCISE 7

The following passage is a ghost story adapted from another letter by Pliny the Younger (*Epistulae* 7.27), in which he describes a supernatural event that happened in Athens. Translate the following passage into English. New vocabulary is listed below the passage.

Erat Athēnīs magna domus sed īnfāmis. Noctū ibi audiēbātur vinculōrum sonus. Deinde cōnspiciēbātur fōrma terribilis. Erat senex macer et squālidus. Capillus eius horrēbat. Vincula gerēbat. Multī, quī in eō aedificiō habitābant, mortuī inveniēbantur. Nēmō causam clādis intellēxit. Tandem domus est dēserta: sōlum id mōnstrum ibi habitābat. Athēnodōrus, philosophus, causam malī intellegere cupīvit. Ibi noctū manēre dēcrēvit. Omnia tunc erant quiēta. Philosophus in tenebrīs manēbat librīsque studēbat. Tunc sonum audīvit vinculōrum. Erat autem Athēnodōrō animus fortis. Philosophus oculōs in librōs intendit, nec mōnstrum cōnspexit, quod ad eum appropinquāvit. Tandem fōrmam mōnstrī terribilem vīdit. Senex macer et squālidus digitō aliquid ostendere vidēbātur, deinde ēvānuit. Postrīdiē philosophus iussit locum effodī, quem umbra senis ostendit. Ibi erant ossa hominis mortuī catēnīs vīncta.

_____

_____

_____

_____

_____

_____

_____

_____

_____

_____

_____

_____

_____

_____

_____

_____

aedificium, aedificiī, *n.* – building
aliquid – something
appropinquō, appropinquāre, appropinquāvī, appropinquātum – to approach
Athēnīs – in Athens
Athēnodōrus, Athēnodōrī, *m.* – Athenodorus
capillus, capillī, *m.* – hair
catēna, catēnae, *f.* – chain
dēsertus, dēserta, dēsertum – deserted
domus, domūs, *f.* – house
effodiō, effodere, effōdī, effossum – to dig up
ēvānēscō, ēvānēscere, ēvānuī, —— – to vanish
horreō, horrēre, horruī, —— – to stick straight out
īnfāmis, īnfāme – of evil repute
intendō, intendere, intendī, intentum – to focus on, to concentrate on

inveniō, invenīre, invēnī, inventum – to discover
macer, macra, macrum – emaciated, very thin
mōnstrum, mōnstrī, *n.* – monster, apparition
mortuus, mortua, mortuum – dead
nēmō (*nom.*) – no one
noctū (*adv.*) – at night
os, ossis, *n.* – bone
philosophus, philosophī, *m.* – philosopher
postrīdiē (*adv.*) – on the next day
quiētus, quiēta, quiētum – quiet
sōlus, sōla, sōlum – only, alone
sonus, sonī, *m.* – sound
squālidus, squālida, squālidum – filthy
terribilis, terribile – terrible, fearful
umbra, umbrae, *f.* – shadow, ghost
vīnctus, vīncta, vīnctum – bound

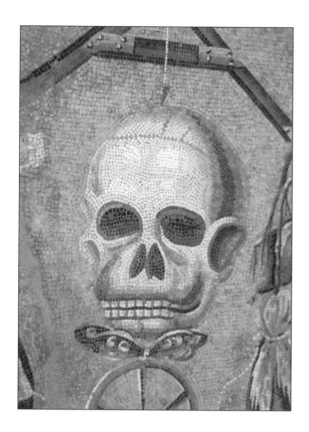

This mosaic of a skull, found in Pompeii, is shown hanging from a plumb line which in turn hangs from a carpenter's level. On one side of the skull (not seen in this photograph) is purple material and a sceptre, which both represent wealth and power. On the other side (cut off in this photograph) is rough material and a beggar's sack, both representing poverty. This balancing of the skull between symbols of wealth and poverty is a reminder that all people, from all walks of life, die. The butterfly and the wheel below the skull represent the fleeting nature of human life.

CONTENT QUESTIONS

After completing Chapter 16, answer these questions.

1. What was Pliny the Younger's position and what are his best known writings?

   _____

   _____

2. Who was Pliny's uncle?

   _____

   _____

3. From what principal part of each verb is the perfect tense formed?

   _____

4. What are the two meanings of the perfect tense?

   _____

   _____

5. Is there any difference in the endings of the perfect active tense for each conjugation?

   _____

6. What two ways to express possession have been studied in this chapter?

   _____

   _____

   _____

CHAPTER 17

▶ EXERCISE 1

Decline the following phrases.

1. *impetus magnus*

	Singular	Plural
Nominative	impetus magnus	impetus magni
Genitive	impetus magni	impetuum magnorum
Dative	impetui magno	impetibus magnis
Accusative	impetum magnum	impetus magnos
Ablative	impetu magno	impetibus magnis
Vocative	impetus magne	impetus magni

2. *gelū* (frost) *ācre*

	Singular	Plural
Nominative	gelu acre	gelua acria
Genitive	gelus acris	geluum acrium
Dative	gelu acri	gelibus acribus
Accusative	gelu acre	gelua acria
Ablative	gelu acri	gelibus acribus
Vocative	gelu acre	gelua acria

▶ EXERCISE 2

Complete the sentence, fill in the blank, or answer the question, all based on derivation.

1. From what Latin noun do we derive "cornucopia"?

   a. festival

   b. food

   c. horn

   d. holiday

2. Which constellation is named for the horn of a goat?

   a. Sagittarius

   b. Capricorn

   c. Aquarius

   d. Gemini

3. All of the following are derived from *cornū* **EXCEPT**

    a. cornice

    b. corona

    c. cornet

    d. corner

4. All of the following are derived from the Latin word for "house" **EXCEPT**

    a. danger

    b. dungeon

    c. madame

    d. maddened

5. A "major-domo" is

    a. the most important player on a team.

    b. in charge of a large household.

    c. a rank in the American military.

    d. the owner of a gambling casino.

6. Which of the following is **imperative** for almost all college graduates?

    a. to go to the beach

    b. to find a job

    c. to visit relatives

    d. to move back home

7. What term would be used for dynasties like the Flavians of Rome?

    a. democratic

    b. legislative

    c. matriarchal

    d. imperial

8. Choose the **ANTONYM** of "impetuous."

    a. precipitate

    b. spontaneous

    c. fervid

    d. circumspect

9. Which of the following is **NOT** derived from the same Latin root as "impetuous"?

    a. petulant

    b. petition

    c. petty

    d. perpetual

10. Which of the following is derived from the preposition *in* and the verb meaning "to go"?

    a. imperial

    b. initial

    c. impetuous

    d. incendiary

11. What is a "sinecure"?

    a. a job with no responsibility

    b. a building with no codes

    c. a con artist

    d. a street vendor

12. A mild command is expressed by a(n) _____.

    a. imperative

    b. infinitive

    c. jussive

    d. participle

13. Which of the following is **NOT** derived from *locus*?

    a. lieutenant

    b. locative

    c. locomotive

    d. locust

14. What is an "amanuensis"?

    a. a secretary

    b. an ambidextrous person

    c. one with small motor skills

    d. a wounded warrior

15. All of the following are derived from *manus* **EXCEPT**

    a. manure

    b. manatee

    c. mantle

    d. maneuver

16. In Poe's story "The Cask of Amontillado," the skeleton found chained to the **wall** had been

    a. incinerated

    b. immured

    c. impetrated

    d. inhumed

17. A **mural** is _____.

    a. painted by hand

    b. large in size

    c. a gift presented to the city

    d. drawn on a wall

18. Which of the following is **NOT** a **SYNONYM** for "tumult"?

    a. swelling

    b. disorder

    c. turbulence

    d. excitement

19. Which of the following is **NOT** derived from the Latin word for "wind"?

    a. ventilation

    b. ventrical

    c. vent

    d. ventiduct

20. All of the following are derived from *alō* **EXCEPT**

    a. alimony

    b. adolescence

    c. alien

    d. adult

21. The root for the Latin verb meaning "to lose" is also found in _____.

    a. misery

    b. miscible

    c. ominous

    d. omission

22. What is the Latin root of the verb *corripiō*?

    a. *rapiō*

    b. *rumpō*

    c. *rubeō*

    d. *rabiō*

23. Which of the following is **NOT** derived from the Latin verb meaning "to run"?

    a. cursor

    b. cursory

    c. curse

    d. cursive

24. A method of writing that joins letters together in flowing script is called _____.

    a. block lettering

    b. abbreviating

    c. cursive

    d. printing

25. Which of the following is **NOT** derived from *currō*?

    a. curious

    b. currency

    c. recourse

    d. recurrence

26. The student gave a **cursory** look at the assignment.

    a. close

    b. quick

    c. intent

    d. unconcerned

27. The root of *exstinguō* means _____.

    a. to close

    b. to touch

    c. to cover

    d. to set on fire

28. All of the following are derived from *iaciō* **EXCEPT**

    a. adjacent

    b. adjective

    c. jetty

    d. jut

29. From which word is "tentative" derived?

    a. *tempus*

    b. *tendō*

    c. *temptō*

    d. *teneō*

30. Which of the following does **NOT** belong by derivation?

    a. tentacle

    b. attempt

    c. pretentious

    d. temptation

▶ EXERCISE 3

Conjugate the following verbs in the pluperfect active and translate each form.

1. *currō, currere, cucurrī, cursum*

Pluperfect Active: *currō*

	Singular		Plural	
First person	cucurreram	I had run	cucurreramus	we had run
Second person	cucurreras	you had run	cucurreratis	y'all had run
Third person	cucurrerat	he/she/it had run	cucurrerant	they had run

2. *iaciō, iacere, iēcī, iactum*

Pluperfect Active: *iaciō*

	Singular		Plural	
First person	ieceram	I had thrown	ieceramus	we had thrown
Second person	ieceras	you had thrown	ieceratis	y'all had thrown
Third person	iecerat	he/she/it had thrown	iecerant	they had thrown

3. *dēvastō, dēvastāre, dēvastāvī, dēvastātum*

Pluperfect Active: *dēvastō*

	Singular		Plural	
First person	devastaveram	I had devastated	devastaveramus	we had devastated
Second person	devastaveras	you had devastated	devastaveratis	y'all had devastated
Third person	devastaverat	he/she/it had devastated	devastaverant	they had devastated

▶ EXERCISE 4

Translate the Latin into English and the English into Latin.

1. potuerātis   *y'all had been able*
2. fuerāmus   *we had been*
3. corripuerāmus   *we had engulfed*
4. you had tried   *temptāverās*
5. iēcerat   *he/she/it had thrown*
6. you (plural) had lost   *amīserātis*
7. exstīnxerant   *they had extinguished*
8. alueram   *I had feed*
9. you (plural) had run *cucurrerātis*
10. you had been   *fuerās*

The following three exercises are based on the works of the historian Suetonius (ca. 70–150 CE) who lived somewhat later than Tacitus and is less famous than Tacitus. The imperial bureaucracy was a major institution in his day, and his works reflect this condition. He wrote *Dē vītā Caesarum* (*On the Lives of the Emperors*), biographies of the emperors between Caesar and Domitian, and *Dē virīs illūstribus* (*On Famous Men*), biographies of Roman poets, historians, and rhetors. Suetonius's lives of the emperors make entertaining reading. He loves gossip, and likes to dwell on unsavory details of their personal lives. It is interesting that even in the case of emperors whom Suetonius presumably admired he makes no attempt to whitewash their characters. He presents their achievements and faults equally. Suetonius follows certain patterns: for example, he regularly recounts a person's last words. He exposes facts without historical judgment. His work strongly influenced the tradition of medieval biography.

TIMELINE:
44 BCE–murder of Iūlius Caesar
27 BCE–14 CE emperor Augustus
14 CE–37 CE emperor Tiberius
37 CE–41 CE emperor Caligula
41 CE–54 CE emperor Claudius
54 CE–68 CE emperor Nerō

The assassins rush at and kill Julius Caesar on the Ides of March, 44 BCE. On this ominous date, the Senate was scheduled to meet at the Theatre of Pompey.

▶ EXERCISE 5

Translate the following text into English.

Deī dīxerant Caesarī Īdūs Mārtiās eī allātūrās esse clādem. Īdibus Mārtiīs Caesar in senātum intrāvit et dīxit: "Īdūs Mārtiae iam vēnērunt, sed clādēs nōn vēnit." Tunc homō Caesarī respondit: "Īdūs Mārtiae fortasse iam vēnērunt, sed nōndum discessērunt." Mox hominēs Caesarem gladiīs occīdērunt. Caesar vīdit inter eōs esse amīcum suum Brūtum et ante mortem exclāmāvit: "Et tū, Brute!"

_____

_____

_____

_____

_____

_____

allātūrās esse (future infinitive) – would bring
Brūtus, Brūtī, _m._ – Brutus
Caesar, Caesaris, _m._ – Caesar
exclāmō, exclāmāre, exclāmāvī, exclāmātum – to exclaim
Īdūs, Īduum, _f. pl._ – Ides (the 13th or the 15th day of every month); **Īdibus Mārtiīs** – on the Ides of March, i.e., on March 15th

inter + _acc._ – among
Mārtius, Mārtia, Mārtium – belonging to the month of March
nōndum (_adv._) – not yet
senātus, senātūs, _m._ – senate

Tiberius Caesar Augustus, second Julio-Claudian emperor of Rome.

▶ EXERCISE 6

Translate the following text into Latin.

The emperor Augustus had already departed from life. The new emperor was Tiberius. Everything was in confusion. People had to show tears because of the death of the emperor and joy because of the new emperor. Then everybody had to swear that they desired always to obey the emperor and to have only that freedom which the emperor had given.

_____

_____

_____

_____

_____

_____

Augustus, Augustī, *m.* – Augustus
iūrō, iūrāre, iūrāvī, iūrātum – to swear, to take an oath
lībertās, lībertātis, *f.* – freedom
obtemperō, obtemperāre, obtemperāvī, obtemperātum
  + *dat.* – to obey someone

sōlum (*adv.*) – only
Tiberius, Tiberiī, *m.* – Tiberius

Bust of the third Julio-Claudian emperor Gāius Caligula.

▶ EXERCISE 7

Translate the following text into English.

Caligula semper temptābat pecūniam ex Rōmānīs corripere. Multī hominēs, quī timēbant, Caligulam hērēdem suum nuncupāverant. Sī eī vīvere pergēbant, imperātor fortī īrā capiēbātur et putābat eōs esse dērīsōrēs. Itaque eīs cuppēdiās, quās venēnāverat, mittere solēbat.

_____

_____

_____

_____

_____

_____

Caligula, Caligulae, *m.* – Caligula
cuppēdiae, cuppēdiārum, *f. pl.* – dainty dishes, delicacies
dērīsor, dērīsōris, *m.* – mocker
hērēs, hērēdis, *m.* – heir
nuncupō, nuncupāre, nuncupāvī, nuncupātum – to nominate

pecūnia, pecūniae, *f.* – money
pergō, pergere, perrēxī, perrēctum – to continue
sī – if
venēnō, venēnāre, venēnāvī, venēnātum – to poison

CONTENT QUESTIONS

After completing Chapter 17, answer these questions.

1. The pluperfect endings for all conjugations look like what other verb tense?

   _____

2. How do you translate the pluperfect?

   _____

3. What is the characteristic vowel in the fourth declension?

   _____

4. In which case do the neuter nouns of the fourth declension have a different ending from the masculine and feminine nouns (besides the nominative, the accusative, and the vocative)?

   _____

5. What is the subject of Tacitus's "Dialogue about Orators"?

   _____

6. When was the great fire in Rome? What caused it?

   _____

CHAPTER 18

▶ EXERCISE 1

Conjugate the following verbs in the future perfect active and translate each form.

1. *excitō, excitāre, excitāvī, excitātum*

Future Perfect Active: *excitō*

Singular

First person   _____   _____

Second person   _____   _____

Third person   _____   _____

Plural

First person   _____   _____

Second person   _____   _____

Third person   _____   _____

2. *mittō, mittere, mīsī, missum*

Future Perfect Active: *mittō*

Singular

First person   _____   _____

Second person   _____   _____

Third person   _____   _____

Plural

First person   _____   _____

Second person   _____   _____

Third person   _____   _____

3. *fugiō, fugere, fūgī, ——*

Future Perfect Active: *fugiō*

Singular

First person   _____   _____

Second person   _____   _____

Third person   _____   _____

Plural

First person   _____   _____

Second person   _____   _____

Third person   _____   _____

▶ EXERCISE 2

Choose the word that does **NOT** belong by derivation.

1. a. deify   b. adieu   c. divine   d. address

2. a. diary   b. joust   c. dismal   d. journey

3. a. facetious   b. facial   c. facet   d. facade

4. a. fatal   b. prefatory   c. fatigue   d. fated

5. a. martial   b. married   c. marital   d. marriage

6. a. meridian   b. sundial   c. merit   d. sojourn

7. a. patrician   b. patter   c. patron   d. patent

8. a. reality   b. reptile   c. really   d. republic

9. a. somnambulism   b. insomniac   c. somnolent   d. sommelier

10. a. oxymoron   b. uxoricide   c. uxorial   d. uxorious

11. a. agriculture   b. colony   c. accolade   d. cult

12. a. dormant   b. dormouse   c. dormer   d. dormitory

13. a. duplicity   b. duct   c. duchy   d. deduction

14. a. succinct   b. excite   c. solicitous   d. recital

15. a. occultism   b. cellar   c. accelerate   d. occult

16. a. query   b. acquiesce   c. conquest   d. exquisite

17. a. postern   b. puny   c. posterity   d. pungent

▶ EXERCISE 3

Decline the following phrase.

1.   *bona fidēs (fidēs, fideī, f. – faith)*

	Singular	**Plural**
Nominative	_____	_____
Genitive	_____	_____
Dative	_____	_____
Accusative	_____	_____
Ablative	_____	_____
Vocative	_____	_____

▶ EXERCISE 4

Fill in the blanks with the correct form of the verb in parentheses and translate the completed sentence.

Example: Sī ____potueris____ ad mē venīre, magnum gaudium habēbō. (possum)
If you can come to me, I will have great joy.

1.   Cum epistulam meam _____, ad eam respondēre dēbēbis. (legō)

_____

2.   Sī uxor marītum _____, amor eam corripiet. (cōnspiciō)

_____

3.   Sī fāta _____, timēbimusne? (sciō)

_____

4.   Cum eum tumultum _____, fugiēs. (videō)

_____

5.   Cum domum _____, dormiēmus. (intrō)

_____

▶ EXERCISE 5

Translate into Latin.

1.   Wait for the day!   _____

2.   I kept reading for many days.   _____

3.   These faces are renowned (famous).   _____

4.   We will eat at midday (*use a simple ablative*).   _____

5.   With what things did you (plural) give us help?   _____

6.   I am eager for good things.   _____

The Roman author Petronius, who lived at the time of the emperor Nero (ca. 27–66 CE), is the author of another novel-like work, which is in some respects similar to Apuleius's *Golden Ass*. Its title is *Satyricon*, a satiric prose account (intertwined with some poetry) of the adventures of a group of friends in southern Italy. Only fragments of the *Satyricon* still survive, though many of these fragments are quite large.

Petronius was Nero's advisor and, because of his taste for sophistication, called *arbiter ēlegantiārum* ("judge of refinement"). Nero had a habit of turning against friends, many of whom he suspected of sedition or plotting against him. Petronius too became the object of the emperor's anger and he was ordered to commit suicide. Before his death Petronius lampooned the emperor in his will. A copy was sent to Nero.

Romans reclining at a lavish banquet while slaves
serve food and entertainment is being offered.

▶ EXERCISE 6

In the sentences below, you will see a partial description of the famous *Cēna Trimalchiōnis*, "Trimalchio's dinner," a lavish dinner-party described in *Satyricon*. In this exercise, your viewpoint is that of someone who has already attended similar parties and predicts what will happen at this one. Combine each pair of simple sentences into one complex sentence containing a *cum* clause. Use the appropriate verb tense. Then translate the newly formed sentence. The adverb *posteā* will disappear in the complex sentence. Use the appropriate verb tense and translate the newly formed sentence.

Example: Ad casam veniētis. Posteā intrābitis.
Cum ad casam vēneritis, intrābitis.
When you come to the cottage, you will come in.

1.   Servī aquam dabunt. Posteā manūs lavābitis.
        lavō, lavāre, lāvī, lōtum – to wash   **servus, servī,** *m.* – slave

        _____

        _____

2.   Manūs lavābitis. Posteā gustātiōnem magnam habēbitis.
        gustātiō, gustātiōnis, *f.* – appetizer

        _____

        _____

3.   Gustātiōnem magnam habēbitis. Posteā ōva comedētis.
        ōvum, ōvī, *n.* – egg

        _____

        _____

4. Ōva comedētis. Posteā vīnum bibētis.
   bibō, bibere, bibī, —— ** – to drink   **vīnum, vīnī, *n.* – wine

   _____

   _____

5. Vīnum bibētis. Posteā leporem comedētis.
   lepus, leporis, *m.* – rabbit

   _____

   _____

6. Leporem comedētis. Posteā servī aprum vōbīs pōnent.
   aper, aprī, *m.* – boar

   _____

   _____

7. Servī aprum vōbīs pōnent. Posteā fābulās nārrābitis.

   _____

   _____

These types of amphoras and other vessels might have been used
to serve and store food and beverages. This drawing is based
on excavations in Herculaneum and Pompeii where such
items were found in situ.

▶ EXERCISE 7

The following text, adapted from *Satyricon*, is a story of the type called "Milesian tale": a funny short story featuring love and adventure. Translate the following text into English.

Mulier marītum suum āmīserat et dē eō valdē dolēbat. Corpus marītī, quod in conditōriō iacēbat, tenēbat et lacrimīs cōnsūmēbātur. Propter dolōrem vidua nōn comēdēbat nec dormīre cupiēbat. Prope conditōrium erant trēs latrōnēs crucifīxī, quōrum corpora ā mīlite custōdiēbantur. Mīles vīdit rem in conditōriō movērī et in conditōrium intrāvit. Tunc mulierem cōnspexit et putāvit eam esse mōnstrum. Deinde tamen intellēxit eam esse uxōrem quae dē marītō mortuō dolēbat et cōnsūmēbātur. Tum inquit: "Cibum comedere dēbēs. Sī cibum nōn comēderis, tū quoque mox nōn vīvēs." Cēnam suam dare eī cupiēbat. Fēmina prīmum recūsābat, sed tandem accēpit. Nōn sōlum cibōs comēdit, sed ūnā cum mīlite rīdēbat. Dum mīles cum muliere manēbat, familiārēs ūnīus latrōnis crucifīxī eius corpus clam corripuērunt. Mīles pūnīrī dēbēbat; nam nōn bene custōdīverat. Vidua nōn cupiēbat suum amīcum pūnīrī. Itaque corpus marītī mortuī eī dedit, quod mīles in locum corporis ablātī posuit. Hominēs id crēdere nōn poterant.

_____

_____

_____

_____

_____

_____

_____

_____

_____

_____

_____

_____

ablātus, ablāta, ablātum – taken away
accipiō, accipere, accēpī, acceptum – to accept
cēna, cēnae, *f.* – dinner
cibus, cibī, *m.* – food
clam (*adv.*) – secretly
conditōrium, conditōriī, *n.* – funeral chamber
crucifīxus, crucifīxa, crucifīxum – crucified
custōdiō, custōdīre, custōdīvī, custōdītum – to guard
familiārēs, familiārium, *m. pl.* – family members
latrō, latrōnis, *m.* – criminal, bandit

mōnstrum, mōnstrī, *n.* – monster, apparition
mortuus, mortua, mortuum – dead
prīmum (*adv.*) – at first
pūniō, pūnīre, pūnīvī, pūnītum – to punish
recūsō, recūsāre, recūsāvī, recūsātum – to refuse
reveniō, revenīre, revēnī, reventum – to return
rīdeō, rīdēre, rīsī, rīsum – to laugh
trēs (*nom. m.*) – three
ūnīus – genitive singular of *ūnus*
vidua, viduae, *f.* – widow

CONTENT QUESTIONS

After completing Chapter 18, answer these questions.

1. What new feature appears in the Latin literature in the second century CE?

_____

2. Who are the three "wise" emperors?

_____

3. What is unique about Apuleius's *Golden Ass*?

_____

4. To what forms are the endings of the future perfect very similar?

_____

5. What is the usual gender of the nouns belonging to the fifth declension?

_____

6. What is the characteristic vowel of the nouns of the fifth declension?

_____

CHAPTER 19

▶ EXERCISE 1

Decline the following phrases.

1. *haec barba*

	Singular	**Plural**
Nominative	_____	_____
Genitive	_____	_____
Dative	_____	_____
Accusative	_____	_____
Ablative	_____	_____

2. *hoc proelium*

	Singular	**Plural**
Nominative	_____	_____
Genitive	_____	_____
Dative	_____	_____
Accusative	_____	_____
Ablative	_____	_____

▶ EXERCISE 2

Match the meaning of the Latin root in Column B to the word in Column A that is derived from that root. Some meanings may be used more than once.

Column A

1. _____ herbicide
2. _____ carnival
3. _____ invulnerable
4. _____ apricot
5. _____ preside
6. _____ foreign
7. _____ intern
8. _____ assiduous
9. _____ increment
10. _____ investor
11. _____ arbor
12. _____ barbed
13. _____ insane
14. _____ tribulation
15. _____ accelerate
16. _____ enter
17. _____ cuisine
18. _____ travesty
19. _____ carnivorous
20. _____ precocious
21. _____ accrue
22. _____ survival
23. _____ forfeit
24. _____ concrete
25. _____ incarnation
26. _____ surplice
27. _____ terrible
28. _____ sedate
29. _____ intimate
30. _____ vivacious
31. _____ forest

Column B

A. clothes
B. grow
C. swiftly
D. beard
E. wound
F. outside
G. plant
H. cook
I. between
J. heal
K. meat
L. fierce
M. rub
N. hide
O. live
P. sit
Q. terrifying

32. _____ contrite

33. _____ insidious

34. _____ recruit

35. _____ feral

36. _____ biscuit

37. _____ vestment

38. _____ kitchen

39. _____ siege

40. _____ sanatorium

41. _____ vitamin

42. _____ detriment

43. _____ assessment

▶ EXERCISE 3

Conjugate the following verbs in the perfect passive and translate each form.

1. *sānō, sānāre, sānāvī, sānātum*

Perfect Passive: *sānō*

Singular

First person	_____	_____
Second person	_____	_____
Third person	_____	_____

Plural

First person	_____	_____
Second person	_____	_____
Third person	_____	_____

2. *dūcō, dūcere, dūxī, ductum*

Perfect Passive: *dūcō*

Singular

First person	_____	_____
Second person	_____	_____
Third person	_____	_____

Plural

First person	_____	_____
Second person	_____	_____
Third person	_____	_____

▶ EXERCISE 4

Fill in the blanks in the following sentences with the correct form of the perfect passive participle of the verbs whose infinitives are in parentheses. Translate each sentence, once using the longer literal translation and a second time using the shortened literal translation.

Example: In vulneribus ___sānātīs___ cicātrīcēs manent. (sānāre)
The scars stay on the wounds having been healed.   The scars stay on the healed wounds.

1. In epistulā _____ nōn multa verba sunt. (mittere)

    _____

    _____

2. Fortitūdō Germānōrum _____ manēbat. (relinquere)
    Germānus, Germānī, *m.* – German

    _____

    _____

3. Casās ab Hūnīs _____ nōn vidēmus. (aedificāre)
    Hūnus, Hūnī, *m.* – Hun

    _____

    _____

4. Mīlitēs Germānōrum ad bellum _____ nōn timēmus. (parāre)

    _____

    _____

5. Fēminae ā Rōmānīs _____, deinde _____ ad Germānōs fūgērunt. (capere) (līberāre)

    _____

    _____

6. Suntne haec vestīmenta mīlitum _____? (vulnerāre)

    _____

    _____

The Huns are pictured marching through Gaul, plundering this Roman province.

▶ EXERCISE 5

Fill in the blanks in the following sentences with the correct form of the demonstrative pronoun/adjective *hic, haec, hoc*. Translate the sentences.

Example: _____Haec_____ cōnsilia semper audiuntur.
These counsels/plans are always heard.

1. In _____ equīs semper manent Hūnī.

   _____

2. Dē _____ herbā nihil scīmus.

   _____

3. _____ hominum magnam fortitūdinem vidēmus.

   _____

4. Hoc est _____ fēminae cōnsilium novum.

   _____

5. In _____ nūbe nihil vidērī potest.

   _____

6. _____ herbae captae sunt ex agrīs.

   _____

7. _____ rēgīnae praeclārae dōna dabimus.

   _____

Attila and the Huns were master horsemen. Here you see the Huns on horseback attacking. Attila and the Huns drove the Roman emperor Valentinian III from Ravenna in 452 CE. Although he reached Rome, Attila did not invade the city. According to tradition, Pope Leo persuaded him to spare the city.

▶ EXERCISE 6

Change the perfect active verb into the perfect passive. Use the ablative of agent or instrument in the changed sentences where needed. Then translate the changed sentence.

Example: Herbās ex hīs agrīs cēpimus.
Herbae ex hīs agrīs ā nōbīs captae sunt.   The plants were/have been taken from these fields by us.

1. Dē Hūnīs nōn multa audīvimus.

   _____

   _____

2. Germānī mīlitēs fēminārum cōnsilia exspectāvērunt.

   _____

   _____

3. Vōs, amīcī, saepe vocāvī.

   _____

   _____

4. Ducēs nōs hanc urbem capere iussērunt.

   _____

   _____

5. Hanc carnem numquam coximus.

   _____

   _____

6. Castra Hūnōrum cōnspeximus.

   _____

   _____

▶ EXERCISE 7

Translate the following questions. Then choose the best answer for each and translate. The Reading Vocabulary in Chapter 19 may be consulted.

1. Cūr Hūnī nōn sōlum gladiōs sed etiam laqueōs in proeliō habent?

    Hūnī laqueīs et gladiīs pugnant.

    Hūnī hostēs laqueīs occidere solent.

    Nōn est eīs difficile hostēs laqueīs captōs gladiīs occīdere.

    _____

    _____

    _____

2. Ubi (*where*) habitant Hūnī?

    Hūnī casās habent.

    Hūnī forīs vīvunt.

    Hūnī ubīque terribilēs vidērī cupiunt.

    _____

    _____

    _____

3. Quās rēs in equīs faciunt Hūnī?

    In equīs comedunt, in equīs dormiunt, in equīs pugnant.

    Sine equīs Hūnī impetūs in hostēs facere solent.

    Hūnī saepe ab equīs sēparantur.

    _____

    _____

    _____

4. Solentne Hūnī carnem coquere?

    Carō ā Hūnīs nōn comeditur.

    Hūnī vestīmenta ex animālium pellibus facta gerunt.

    Carō ā Hūnīs nōn coquitur, sed paulisper teritur.

    _____

    _____

    _____

5. Ubi crēscunt herbae, quārum rādīcēs comedere solent Hūnī?

    Herbae, quārum rādīcēs comedere solent Hūnī, in agrīs cōnspiciuntur.

    Hūnī rādīcēs herbārum et animālium carnem comedere solent.

    Hūnī vestīmenta ex animālium pellibus facta gerunt.

_____

_____

_____

6. Cūr Hūnī terribilēs vidērī timōremque in aliīs hominibus excitāre cupiunt?

    Faciēs Hūnōrum cōnsultō vulnerantur.

    Hūnī pulchram fōrmam habēre cupiunt.

    Hūnī sunt hominēs ferī et ferōcēs.

_____

_____

_____

Attila the Hun lived from 406 to 453 CE. As Khan of
the Huns, he was the leader of the Hunnic Empire
and known for his ferocity and savagery.

CONTENT QUESTIONS

After completing Chapter 19, answer these questions.

1. How does the participle behave like both a verb and an adjective?

    _____

2. What part of speech is *hic, haec, hoc*?

    _____

3. How is the perfect passive indicative of any verb formed?

    _____

4. Ammianus Marcellinus wrote his history as a continuation of the work of which historian?

    _____

5. What were the effects of the movements of the Huns in the third and fourth centuries CE?

    _____

    _____

6. When did the Huns themselves enter the Roman Empire?

    _____

CHAPTER 20

▶ EXERCISE 1

Conjugate the following verbs in the pluperfect passive and translate each form.

1. *pūniō, pūnīre, pūnīvī, pūnītum*

Pluperfect Passive: *pūniō*

Singular

First person _____ _____

Second person _____ _____

Third person _____ _____

Plural

First person _____ _____

Second person _____ _____

Third person _____ _____

2. *dēlectō, dēlectāre, dēlectāvī, dēlectātum*

Pluperfect Passive: *dēlectō*

Singular

First person _____ _____

Second person _____ _____

Third person _____ _____

Plural

First person _____ _____

Second person _____ _____

Third person _____ _____

▶ EXERCISE 2

Complete the sentence, fill in the blank, or answer the question, all according to derivation.

1. The word "adolescence" is derived from the Latin root meaning _____.

   a. grieve
   b. nourish
   c. change
   d. allow

2. Which of the following is derived from *cor*?

   a. scourge
   b. corsage
   c. coruscate
   d. courage

3. All of the following are derived from the Latin word for "heart" **EXCEPT**

   a. core
   b. cordial
   c. cornea
   d. record

4. The word "ferret" is derived from _____.

   a. *ferō*
   b. *fūr*
   c. *ferus*
   d. *fūriōsus*

5. What is the meaning of the Latin word from which we derive "furtive"?

   a. thief
   b. rage
   c. secret
   d. dark

6. All of the following derive from the Latin word meaning "law" **EXCEPT**

   a. loyal
   b. privilege
   c. legacy
   d. legible

7. Who was the Roman deity of orchards?

   a. Faunus
   b. Janus
   c. Pomona
   d. Athena

8. The word "pomegranate" is derived from the Latin root meaning _____.

   a. fruit
   b. sweet
   c. hard
   d. boundary

9. The **pommel** of a saddle is so-called because it is shaped like a(n) _____.

   a. foot
   b. apple
   c. horn
   d. hook

10. Which of the following is **NOT** derived from *aequus*?

   a. qualify
   b. adequate
   c. inequality
   d. equatorial

11. Choose the **SYNONYM** of "equivocal."

   a. even

   b. just

   c. dubious

   d. cowardly

12. The word "divine" is related by derivation to _____.

   a. diary

   b. device

   c. dive

   d. deist

13. The word "human" is related by derivation to _____.

   a. humble

   b. homage

   c. humorous

   d. hospitable

14. Which of the following would be described as **impoverished**?

   a. the prince

   b. the miser

   c. the pauper

   d. the merchant

15. Which of the following is **NOT** derived from the Latin word meaning "full"?

   a. pluperfect

   b. accomplish

   c. deplete

   d. plenty

16. A **plenary** session of Congress

   a. is unable to pass legislation.

   b. is attended by all qualified members.

   c. meets behind closed doors.

   d. is faced with a full agenda.

17. The word "abundance" is related by derivation to _____.

   a. inundate

   b. reunion

   c. penumbra

   d. unduly

18. A **dilettante** is one who

   a. is easy to train.

   b. lives a fruitful life.

   c. takes delight in fine art.

   d. leaves an indelible impression.

19. An **indigent** person is _____.

   a. native-born

   b. poor

   c. considered unworthy

   d. angry

20. All of the following are derived from *lūdō* **EXCEPT**

   a. illusion

   b. elusive

   c. prelude

   d. luster

21. Hackers are breaking into secure computers with **impunity**.

   a. without difficulty

   b. without training

   c. without punishment

   d. without detection

22. In the word "photography," which syllable is in the **penultimate** position?

   a. pho

   b. tog

   c. ra

   d. phy

▶ EXERCISE 3

Decline the following phrases.

1. *ille fūr*

	Singular	**Plural**
Nominative	ille fur	illi fures
Genitive	illius furis	illorum furum
Dative	illi furi	illis furibus
Accusative	illum furem	illos fures
Ablative	illo fure	illis furibus

2. *illud fūrtum*

	Singular	**Plural**
Nominative	ille furtum	illi furta
Genitive	illius furti	illorum furtorum
Dative	illi furto	illis furtis
Accusative	illum furtum	illos furta
Ablative	illo furto	illis furtis

▶ EXERCISE 4

Change the following sentences from the active to the passive voice and translate the revised sentence.

Example: Dolor mē corripuerat.
Dolōre eram correptus/–a.
I had been seized by pain.

1. Aequō animō illās rēs tolerāveram.
   tolerō, tolerāre, tolerāvī, tolerātum – to tolerate

   _____

   _____

2. Pauperēs omnia āmīserant.

   _____

   _____

3. Liber ille dē rēbus hūmānīs et dīvīnīs nōs docuerat.

   _____

   _____

4. Urbēs timōris plēnās vīderātis.

   _____

   _____

▶ EXERCISE 5

Fill in the blanks with the correct perfect infinitive using the verb in parentheses. Translate the sentences.

Example: Augustīnus nārrat sē nōn bonum adulēscentem ____fuisse____. (esse)
Augustine tells that he was not a good young man.

1. Augustīnus tamen dīcit sē propter fūrtum nōn _____. (pūniō)

   _____

2. Augustīnus intellēxit rēs malās ā sē _____. (faciō)

   _____

3. Augustīnus sciēbat sē nōn _____ pōma aliōrum hominum capere. (dēbeō)

   _____

4. Augustīnus intellēxit adulēscentēs pōma capta nōn _____. (dēlectō)

   _____

5. Augustīnus dīcit sē et suōs amīcōs rēs malās facere _____. (cupiō)

   _____

Aurēlius Augustīnus, known as Augustine,
bishop of Hippo, seated here with a child
named Adeodatus, perhaps his son.

▶ EXERCISE 6

Translate into Latin.

1. Augustine had sought the tree with his friends during the night.
   Augustīnus, Augustīnī, *m.* – Augustine

   _____

2. The tree had been sought by Augustine and his friends during the night.

   _____

3. The young men had done many bad things.

   _____

4. Many bad things had been done by the young men.

   _____

5. They had left all the fruits.

   _____

6. All the fruits had been left by them.

   _____

▶ EXERCISE 7

Translate the following passage into English. It has been adapted from Augustine's *Confessions*.

Litterās Graecās nōn valdē amābam. Nam litterīs Latīnīs puer eram alitus et eās amāveram. Verba tamen Graeca difficilia mihi vidēbantur. Ex litterīs Latīnīs meminī mē maximē esse dēlectātum dē Aenēā et dē Dīdōne legere. Legēbam Aenēam rēgīnam relīquisse et ad Italiam nāvigāvisse et dolēbam. Legēbam omnia misera Dīdōnī esse vīsa et eam sē occīdisse et dolēbam. Illa fābula animum meum semper movēbat et eā dēlectābar. Sed dē vītā meā nōn cōgitābam nec cōgitābam mē dēbēre rēs bonās quaerere et bonum esse. Putō illīs temporibus mē potuisse tantum dē librīs Latīnīs cōgitāre.

_____

_____

_____

_____

_____

_____

_____

_____

_____

Aenēās, Aenēae, *m.* – Aeneas
Dīdō, Dīdōnis, *f.* – Dido
Graecus, Graeca, Graecum – Greek
Italia, Italiae, *f.* – Italy

Latīnus, Latīna, Latīnum – Latin
maximē (*adv.*) – especially
meminī, meminisse – to remember (defective verb: past forms have present meaning)

Dido is reclining on a couch across from Aeneas. Dido embraces Aeneas's son Ascanius while her sister and confidant Anna looks on.

CONTENT QUESTIONS

After completing Chapter 20, answer these questions.

1. What are Augustine's *Confessions* about?

   They are about Augustine's sinful childhood.

2. Where was Augustine born?

   Augustine was born in Thagast (modern day Algeria)

3. In what way are the perfect and pluperfect passive indicatives similar, and in what way are they different?

   They both consist of two words and have a form of the word "to be". Additionally, they have the same endings for the first word. Pluperfect passive is translated as had been __ed while perfect passive is translated as have __ed. Pluperfect passive also uses the imp. form

4. How are the perfect active and the perfect passive infinitives different in appearance? of "to be" while perfect passive uses the pres. form

   Perfect active consists of the 4th pp + the perfect active endings, while the perfect passive consists of the 4th pp the the perfect passive endings and an imperfect form of "to be". Usually perfect passive is a word more than perfect active.

5. Where are the perfect infinitives mainly used?

   They are mainly used with words like poteram and volo.

6. What are the differences in the meaning of *hic, haec, hoc* and *ille, illa, illud*?

   Hic, haec, hoc means this/these. Ille, illa, illud means that/those. Hic, haec, hoc is used for things nearby, while ille, illa, illud is used for things relatively far away.

7. What is the dual use of *hic, haec, hoc* and *ille, illa, illud*?

   They can be used interchangeably.

CHAPTER 21

▶ EXERCISE 1

Conjugate the following verbs in the future perfect passive and translate each form.

1. *accipiō, accipere, accēpī, acceptum*

Future Perfect Passive: *accipiō*

Singular

First person   _____   _____

Second person   _____   _____

Third person   _____   _____

Plural

First person   _____   _____

Second person   _____   _____

Third person   _____   _____

2. *accūsō, accūsāre, accūsāvī, accūsātum*

Future Perfect Passive: *accūsō*

Singular

First person   _____   _____

Second person   _____   _____

Third person   _____   _____

Plural

First person   _____   _____

Second person   _____   _____

Third person   _____   _____

▶ EXERCISE 2

Complete the sentence, fill in the blank, or answer the question, all based on derivation.

1. An **axial** skeleton consists of _____.

   a. arms and legs
   b. legs and trunk
   c. trunk and head
   d. head and arms

2. Which of the following is derived from the same Latin root as "constancy"?

   a. obstacle
   b. content
   c. contaminate
   d. tacit

3. Which goddess was the "Lady Luck" of the Roman pantheon?

   a. Pomona
   b. Fortuna
   c. Minerva
   d. Vesta

4. Which of the following does **NOT** belong by derivation?

   a. honest
   b. honorarium
   c. honorific
   d. hone

5. All of the following are derived from *rota* **EXCEPT**

   a. rowel
   b. roundabout
   c. rouge
   d. rigamarole

6. What is the meaning of the Latin word from which we derive "alien"?

   a. another
   b. allow
   c. nourish
   d. someone

7. All of the following are derived from the same Latin root as "external" **EXCEPT**

   a. stranger
   b. strain
   c. extremist
   d. extraterrestrial

8. From what Latin word is "future" derived?

   a. *fundō*
   b. *futilis*
   c. *sum*
   d. *ūtor*

9. The word "acceptance" is derived from the same Latin root as _____.

   a. achieve
   b. capillary
   c. capsule
   d. anticipate

10. Which of the following is **NOT** derived from *causa*?

    a. caution

    b. accusative

    c. excuse

    d. because

11. All of the following derive from the same Latin root as "descend" **EXCEPT**

    a. condescension

    b. scale

    c. conscience

    d. scan

12. Which of the following does **NOT** belong by derivation?

    a. eruption

    b. douse

    c. interrupt

    d. routine

13. Which of the following could be described as "errant"?

    a. a vagabond

    b. a typo

    c. an eccentric

    d. a fool

14. Which of the following does **NOT** belong by derivation?

    a. immutable

    b. commute

    c. mutilate

    d. mutual

15. The word "assiduous" is derived from the same Latin word as _____.

    a. consider

    b. assign

    c. reservoir

    d. possess

16. What is the meaning of the Latin word from which we derive "extol"?

    a. raise

    b. strike

    c. endure

    d. praise

17. Choose the **SYNONYM** of **animadversion**.

    a. attention

    b. criticism

    c. reverence

    d. deviation

18. What is the meaning of the abbreviation in the sentence "He was born **c.** 1900"?

    a. before

    b. after

    c. around

    d. in

19. The engineer had a **reprehensible** reputation because he

    a. graduated from M.I.T.

    b. always completed a contract on time.

    c. built only bridges.

    d. made so many errors.

20. A person appointed by the court to **take** over someone's property before litigation is called a(n) _____.

    a. receiver   b. achiever

    c. preceptor   d. capitalist

21. From which Latin word do we derive "fortuitous"?

    a. *fors*   b. *forīs*

    c. *for*   d. *fortis*

▶ EXERCISE 3

Decline the future active participle of the following verb.

1. *tollō, tollere, sustulī, sublātum*

Singular

	Masculine	Feminine	Neuter
Nominative	_____	_____	_____
Genitive	_____	_____	_____
Dative	_____	_____	_____
Accusative	_____	_____	_____
Ablative	_____	_____	_____
Vocative	_____	_____	_____

Plural

	Masculine	Feminine	Neuter
Nominative	_____	_____	_____
Genitive	_____	_____	_____
Dative	_____	_____	_____
Accusative	_____	_____	_____
Ablative	_____	_____	_____
Vocative	_____	_____	_____

▶ EXERCISE 4

Translate into Latin.

1. The wheel will have been turned.

   _____

2. You (plural) will have descended.

   _____

3. We will have been rebuked.

   _____

4. You (singular) will have rebuked.

   _____

5. (S)/he will have raised up her/his hand.

   _____

6. You (plural) will have been raised up.

   _____

7. Nothing will have been changed.

   _____

8. I will have changed many things.

   _____

9. The rewards will have been snatched away.

   _____

10. These men will have snatched away the rewards.

    _____

▶ EXERCISE 5

Change the infinitives in the following indirect statements into future infinitives and translate the changed sentences.

Example: Tē multās rēs ā mē accipere crēdō.
Tē multās rēs ā mē acceptūrum/am esse crēdō.
I believe that you will receive many things from me.

1. Nōn multōs hominēs dīvitiās et honōrēs habēre scīmus. *habitūros esse*

   We know that many men will not have riches and honours

   _____

2. Amīcī meī Fortūnam multa mihi dare sed mē nihil possidēre dīcēbant. *daturam esse / possessur*

   My friends were saying that fortune will give many things to me but
   I will possess nothing.

3. Fortūna cōnstantiam sē nōn amāre dīxit.

[handwritten above: amaturam esse]

_____

4. Cīvēs animālia sua prope urbem manēre dīxērunt.

[handwritten above: manhra esse]

The citizens say that their animals will stay near the city.

_____

5. Rēgīna sorōrem suam discēdere nōn putat.

[handwritten above: discessuram esse]

_____

6. Odium numquam esse bonum dīcō.

[handwritten above: futurum esse]

_____

_____

▶ EXERCISE 6

Translate into Latin.

1. On the point of receiving wealth and honors we love Fortune.

_____

2. I say that they are going to receive wealth and honors.

_____

3. On the point of making a mistake we have suddenly been changed.

_____

4. You (singular) said that they would make a mistake.

_____

5. Being about to go down to the sea we observe the ships.

_____

6. Being about to receive gifts they await the queen.

_____

7. We seem to be about to receive gifts.

_____

▶ EXERCISE 7

Translate the following passage into English.

In this passage adapted from his *Cōnsōlātiō Philosophiae* (2.7), Boethius criticizes the earlier Roman view that winning glory for great actions was a way of winning a kind of immortality. According to this view, if one did great deeds, especially in the political or military sphere, these deeds would be always remembered by future generations. This view motivated great Roman statesmen, such as Cicero. But Boethius didn't think much of this idea, as we see here. For him, the only immortality that mattered was immortality of the individual soul.

Sī terra nostra cum magnitūdine tōtīus caelī comparāta erit, vidēbitur esse nihil. Sed terrae pars, in quā habitant hominēs, est valdē parva! In tam parvō spatiō quanta esse potest glōria ūnīus hominis? Et in tam parvō spatiō multae sunt gentēs, multae sunt linguae. Hominēs ūnīus gentis linguās externās nōn saepe intellegunt. Itaque glōria ūnīus hominis ad gentēs externās venīre nōn potest. Sī autem accēperimus glōriam ūnīus hominis in locō valdē parvō mānsūram esse, nec umquam ad gentēs externās ventūram esse, dē tempore quoque cōgitāre dēbēbimus. Sī ūnum temporis pūnctum cum decem mīlibus annōrum comparātum erit, vidēbitur esse nihil. Sī autem decem mīlia annōrum cum tempore īnfīnītō comparāta erunt, vidēbuntur esse nihil. Itaque etiam sī glōria ūnīus hominis per decem mīlia annōrum mānserit, nihil erit. Et glōria, etiam sī per decem mīlia annōrum manēre potuerit, mortālis tandem erit, sicut vīta hominum.

_____

_____

_____

_____

_____

_____

_____

_____

_____

_____

_____

annus, annī, *m.* – year
caelum – means also "universe"
comparō, comparāre, comparāvī, comparātum – to compare (with *cum* + *abl.*)
decem mīlia, mīlium – ten thousand: *decem* has no declensional endings; *mīlia* in the plural is a noun and is joined with the genitive of the word to which it refers
gēns, gentis, *f.* – race, people, nation
glōria, glōriae, *f.* – glory

īnfīnītus, īnfīnīta, īnfīnītum – infinite
lingua, linguae, *f.* – language, tongue
magnitūdō, magnitūdinis, *f.* – vastness, great extent
mortālis, mortāle – mortal, perishable
pūnctum, pūnctī, *n.* – point
quantus, quanta, quantum – how great?
spatium, spatiī, *n.* – space
tōtīus – genitive singular of *tōtus, tōta, tōtum* = all, whole
ūnīus – genitive singular of *ūnus, ūna, ūnum* = one, a single

Anicius Manlius Severīnus Boēthius, ca. 480–ca. 524 CE.

CONTENT QUESTIONS

After completing Chapter 21, answer these questions.

1. When did Boethius live?

   _____

2. What image from Boethius's *Cōnsōlātiō Philosophiae* remained famous for centuries?

   _____

3. How is the future perfect passive of all conjugations formed?

   _____

4. How is the future active participle formed?

   _____

5. How is the future active infinitive formed?

   _____

6. What is the approximate English translation of the future active participle?

   _____

   _____

ENGLISH TO LATIN GLOSSARY

This glossary contains all the **Vocabulary to Learn** from the chapters.

LIST OF ABBREVIATIONS:

(1) = first conjugation
abl. = ablative
acc. = accusative
adj. = adjective
adv. = adverb
conj. = conjunction
dat. = dative
f. = feminine

gen. = genitive
inf. = infinitive
interj. = interjection
m. = masculine
n. = neuter
pl. = plural
prep. = preposition
sg. = singular

NOTE:

The genitive of the words of second declension ending in *–ius* or *–ium* is indicated with a single *ī* which is the ending itself. Note that in the full form there is normally a double *i*: *fīlius, -ī (= fīliī); gaudium, -ī (= gaudiī)*.

A

abandon, relinquō, -ere, relīquī, relictum
abound with, abundō (1) + *abl.*
about, dē, *prep. + abl.*
about to be, futūrus, -a, -um, *participle*
accept, accipiō, -ere, -cēpī, -ceptum
accuse someone of something, accūsō (1) + *acc. + gen.*
adopt, capiō, -ere, cēpī, captum
advice, cōnsilium, -ī, *n.*
after (conj.), cum, *conj.*; postquam, *conj.*
after (prep.), post, *prep. + acc.*
afterward, posteā, *adv.*
against, contrā, *prep. + acc.*; in, *prep. + acc.*
all, omnis, -e, *adj.*
almost, paene, *adv.*
already, iam, *adv.*
also, etiam, *adv.*; quoque, *adv.*
always, semper, *adv.*
among, inter, *prep. + acc.*
and, et, *conj.*; atque, *conj.*; -que, *conj.*
and not, nec, *conj.*
and so, itaque, *conj.*
anger, īra, -ae, *f.*
animal, animal, -ālis, *n.*
another, alius, alia, aliud, *adj.*

answer, respondeō, -ēre, -spondī, -spōnsum
any, ūllus, -a, -um, *adj.*
appearance, fōrma, -ae, *f.*
argument, argūmentum, -ī, *n.*
armed, armātus, -a, -um, *adj.*
around, circum, *prep. + acc.*
ash, cinis, -eris, *m.*
ask, rogō (1)
at home, domī
at last, tandem, *adv.*
at the house of, apud, *prep. + acc.*
athlete, āthlēta, -ae, *m.*
attack, impetus, -ūs, *m.*
await, exspectō (1)
awaken, excitō (1)
away from, ā *or* ab, *prep. + abl.*
axis, axle, axis, -is, *m.*

B

bad, malus, -a, -um, *adj.*
battle, proelium, -ī, *n.*
be, sum, esse, fuī, ——
be able, possum, posse, potuī, ——
be accustomed, soleō, -ēre, solitus sum + *inf.*
be afraid, timeō, -ēre, timuī, ——
be eager for, studeō, -ēre, studuī, —— + *dat.*

be inert, iaceō, -ēre, iacuī, ——
be interested in, studeō, -ēre, studuī, —— + *dat.*
be on fire, ārdeō, -ēre, ārsī, ——
be unwilling, nōlō, *irregular verb*
beard, barba, -ae, *f.*
beautiful, pulcher, pulchra, pulchrum, *adj.*
because of, propter, *prep. + acc.*
beginning, initium, -ī, *n.*
behave, agō, -ere, ēgī, āctum; **(s/he) behaves,** sē gerit
believe somebody, crēdō, -ere, crēdidī, crēditum + *dat.*
between, inter, *prep. + acc.*
blame, reprehendō, -ere, -prehendī, -prehēnsum
blood, sanguis, sanguinis, *m.*
body, corpus, -oris, *n.*
book, liber, librī, *m.*
bosom, gremium, -ī, *n.*
boy, puer, puerī, *m.*
brave, fortis, -e, *adj.*
brook, rīvus, -ī, *m.*
build, aedificō (1)
burn, ārdeō, -ēre, ārsī, ——
but, sed, *conj.*
by, ā *or* ab, *prep. + abl.*

C

call, vocō (1)

camp, castra, -ōrum, *n. pl.*

can, possum, posse, potuī, ——

capture, capiō, -ere, cēpī, captum

care for, cūrō (1)

carry, gerō, -ere, gessī, gestum

cause, causa, -ae, *f.*

cave, spēlunca, -ae, *f.*

chain, vinculum, -ī, *n.*

change, mūtō (1)

chest, pectus, -oris, *n.*

choose, legō, -ere, lēgī, lēctum

citizen, cīvis, -is, *m./f.*

city (city of Rome), urbs, urbis, *f.*

class (of people), classis, -is, *f.*

clothes, vestīmenta, -ōrum, *n. pl.*

cloud, nūbēs, -is, *f.*

combat, proelium, -ī, *n.*

come, veniō, -īre, vēnī, ventum

concerning, dē, *prep. + abl.*

conflagration, incendium, -ī, *n.*

confusion, tumultus, -ūs, *m.*

conquer, vincō, -ere, vīcī, victum

consider, putō (1)

constancy, cōnstantia, -ae, *f.*

consul, cōnsul, -ulis, *m.*

consume, cōnsūmō, -ere, -sūmpsī, -sūmptum

cook, coquō, -ere, coxī, coctum

cottage, casa, -ae, *f.*

country house, vīlla, -ae, *f.*

courage, fortitūdō, -inis, *f.*

crowded, celeber, -bris, -bre, *adj.*

cruel, crūdēlis, -e, *adj.*

cultivate, colō, -ere, coluī, cultum

D

danger, perīculum, -ī, *n.*

darkness, tenebrae, -ārum, *f. pl.*

daughter, fīlia, -ae, *f.*

day, diēs, diēī, *m./f.*

deadly, fūnestus, -a, -um, *adj.*

death, mors, mortis, *f.*

deception, dolus, -ī, *m.*

decide, dēcernō, -ere, -crēvī, -crētum + *inf.*

defeat, vincō, -ere, vīcī, victum

delight, dēliciae, -ārum, *f. pl. (noun)*

delight, dēlectō (1) *(verb)*

descend, dēscendō, -ere, -scendī, -scēnsum

design, parō (1)

desire, cupiō, -ere, -īvī, -ītum

destiny, fātum, -ī, *n.*

destroy, dēleō, -ēre, dēlēvī, dēlētum; tollō, -ere, sustulī, sublātum

determine, dēcernō, -ere, -crēvī, -crētum

devastate, dēvastō (1)

difficult, difficilis, -e, *adj.*

disaster, clādēs, -is, *f.*

distinguished, praeclārus, -a, -um, *adj.*

divine, dīvīnus, -a, -um, *adj.*

do, agō, -ere, ēgī, āctum; faciō, -ere, fēcī, factum

down from, dē, *prep. + abl.*

drive, agō, -ere, ēgī, āctum

during the night, noctū, *adv.*

dwell, habitō (1)

E

each, omnis, -e, *adj.*

easily, facile, *adv.*

eat, comedō, -ere, -ēdī, -ēsum

emperor, imperātor, -ōris, *m.*

enemy, hostis, -is, *m.*

engulf, corripiō, -ere, -ripuī, -reptum

enter, intrō (1)

envy someone, invideō, -ēre, invīdī, invīsum + *dat.*

eruption, incendium, -ī, *n.*

esteem, aestimō (1)

even (adj.), aequus, -a, -um, *adj.*

even (adv.), etiam, *adv.*

ever, umquam, *adv.*

every, omnis, -e, *adj.*

everywhere, ubīque, *adv.*

example, exemplar, -āris, *n.*; exemplum, -ī, *n.*

exceedingly, valdē, *adv.*

exclaim, exclāmō (1)

expect, exspectō (1)

external, externus, -a, -um, *adj.*

extinguish, exstinguō, -ere, exstīnxī, exstīnctum

eye, oculus, -ī, *m.*

F

face, faciēs, -ēī, *f.*

fall, cadō, -ere, cecidī, cāsum

family, familia, -ae, *f.*

famous, praeclārus, -a, -um, *adj.*

far, longē, *adv.*

farmer, agricola, -ae, *m.*

fate, fātum, -ī, *n.*

father, pater, -tris, *m.*

fatherland, patria, -ae, *f.*

fear, timor, -ōris, *m. (noun)*

fear, timeō, -ēre, timuī, —— *(verb)*

feed, alō, -ere, aluī, altum/alitum

feel, sentiō, -īre, sēnsī, sēnsum

feel pain, doleō, -ēre, doluī, ——

ferocious, ferōx, -ōcis, *adj.*

fetter, vinculum, -ī, *n.*

few, paucī, -ae, -a, *pl. adj.*

field, ager, agrī, *m.*

fierce, ācer, ācris, ācre, *adj.*; ferōx, -ōcis, *adj.*

fight, pugnō (1)

finger, digitus, -ī, *m.*

fire, ignis, -is, *m.*

first, prīmus, -a, -um, *adj.*

flame, flamma, -ae, *f.*

flee, fugiō, -ere, fūgī, ——

fleet, classis, -is, *f.*

flesh, carō, carnis, *f.*

flow, fluō, -ere, flūxī, fluxum

for (conj.), enim, *conj.*; nam, *conj.*

for (prep.), prō, *prep. + abl.*

for a long time, diū, *adv.*

for certain, for sure, prō certō, *adverbial phrase*

force, vīs, ——, *f.*, *pl.* vīrēs, vīrium; impetus, -ūs, *m.*

foreign to, aliēnus, -a, -um, *adj.* + *prep.* ā *or* ab + *abl.*

forest, silva, -ae, *f.*

form, fōrma, -ae, *f.*

former, ille, illa, illud

fortunate, fēlīx, -īcis, *adj.*

fortune, fortūna, -ae, *f.*

Fortune, *the goddess* Fortūna, -ae, *f.*

free someone from something, līberō (1) + *acc.* + *abl.*

friend, amīcus, -ī, *m.*

from, ā *or* ab, *prep.* + *abl.*; ē *or* ex, *prep.* + *abl.*

fruit, pōmum, -ī, *n.*

full of, plēnus, -a, -um, *adj.* + *gen.* or + *abl.*

G

garment, vestīmentum, -ī, *n.*

general, dux, ducis, *m.*; imperātor, -ōris, *m.*

geographical places, loca, locōrum, *n. pl.*

get ready, parō (1)

gift, dōnum, -ī, *n.*

girl, puella, -ae, *f.*

give, dō, dăre, dedī, dătum

go away, discēdō, -ere, -cessī, -cessum

go to, petō, -ere, petīvī, petītum

god, deus, -ī, *m.*

goddess, dea, -ae, *f.*

good, bonus, -a, -um, *adj.*

goodbye!, valē!

great, magnus, -a, -um, *adj.*

grief, dolor, -ōris, *m.*

grow, crēscō, -ere, crēvī, ——

H

hand, manus, -ūs, *f.*

happy, fēlīx, -īcis, *adj.*

hatred, odium, -ī, *n.*

have, habeō, -ēre, habuī, habitum

he, is, ea, id, *personal pronoun*

head, caput, -itis, *n.*

head for, petō, -ere, petīvī, petītum

heal, sānō (1)

hear, audiō, -īre, audīvī, audītum

heart, cor, cordis, *n.*

heaven, caelum, -ī, *n.*

help, auxilium, -ī, *n.*

her, suus, -a, -um, *possessive adj.*; eius

herself, sē, *acc. of the reflexive pronoun*

hide, pellis, -is, *f.* (*noun*)

hide, occultō (1) (*verb*)

himself, sē, *acc. of the reflexive pronoun*

his, suus, -a, -um, *possessive adj.*; eius

hold, teneō, -ēre, tenuī, tentum

home, domus, -ūs, *f.*

honor, honor, -ōris, *m.*

horn, cornū, -ūs, *n.*

horse, equus, -ī, *m.*

house, domus, -ūs, *f.*

household, familia, -ae, *f.*

however, autem, *conj.*; tamen, *conj.*

human, hūmānus, -a, -um, *adj.*

human being, homō, -inis, *m.*

hurt, doleō, -ēre, doluī, —— (*intransitive*)

husband, marītus, -ī, *m.*

I

I, ego, *personal pronoun*

I do not care a bit, aestimō ūnīus assis

if, sī, *conj.*

immediately, statim, *adv.*

impetus, impetus, -ūs, *m.*

important, magnus, -a, -um, *adj.*

in, in, *prep.* + *abl.*

in fact, enim, *conj.*; nam, *conj.*

in front of, ante, *prep.* + *acc.*

in such a way, ita, *adv.*

in the open, forīs, *adv.*

inconsistent with, aliēnus, -a, -um, *adj.* + *prep.* ā *or* ab + *abl.*

indication, argūmentum, -ī, *n.*

indifferently, aequō animō

injustice, inīquitās, -ātis, *f.*

into, ad, *prep.* + *acc.*; in, *prep.* + *acc.*

it, is, ea, id, *personal pronoun*

it is allowed to, it is permitted (*for someone to do something*) licet + *dat.* + *inf.*

its, suus, -a, -um, *possessive adj.*; eius

itself, sē, *acc. of the reflexive pronoun*

J

joy, gaudium, -ī, *n.*

judge, iūdex, -icis, *m.* (*noun*)

judge, iūdicō (1) (*verb*)

just, iūstus, -a, -um, *adj.*

just as, sīcut, *adv.*

K

keen, ācer, ācris, ācre, *adj.*

kill, occīdō, -ere, occīdī, occīsum

king, rēx, rēgis, *m.*

know, sciō, scīre, scīvī, scītum

L

lack something, egeō, -ēre, eguī, —— + *abl.*

land, terra, -ae, *f.*

lap, gremium, -ī, *n.*

large, magnus, -a, -um, *adj.*

latter, hic, haec, hoc

law, lēx, lēgis, *f.*

lead, agō, -ere, ēgī, āctum; dūcō, -ere, dūxī, ductum

leader, dux, ducis, *m.*

learned, doctus, -a, -um, *adj.*

leave, discēdō, -ere, -cessī, -cessum

leave behind, relinquō, -ere, relīquī, relictum

legitimate, iūstus, -a, -um, *adj.*

letter (epistle), litterae, -ārum, *f. pl.*; epistula, -ae, *f.*

letter (of the alphabet), littera, -ae, *f.*

lie down, iaceō, -ēre, iacuī, ——

life, vīta, -ae, *f.*

lift up, tollō, -ere, sustulī, sublātum

like, similis, -e, *adj.* + *gen.* or + *dat.*

listen, audiō, -īre, -īvī, -ītum

literature, litterae, -ārum, *f. pl.*

little house, casa, -ae, *f.*

live (be alive), vīvō, -ere, vīxī, vīctum

live (dwell), habitō (1)

long, longus, -a, -um, *adj.*

look at, cōnspiciō, -ere, -spexī, -spectum

look for, quaerō, -ere, quaesīvī, quaesītum

look here!, ecce, *interj.*

lose, āmittō, -ere, -mīsī, -missum

love, amor, -ōris, *m.* (*noun*)

love, amō (1) (*verb*)

M

make, faciō, -ere, fēcī, factum

make a mistake, errō (1)

make a speech, ōrātiōnem habeō

make plans, cōnsilia capiō

man, vir, virī, *m.*

man (i.e., human being), homō, -inis, *m.*

many, multus, -a, -um, *adj.*

matter, rēs, reī, *f.*

meat, carō, carnis, *f.*

meet, conveniō, -īre, -vēnī, -ventum

memory, memoria, -ae, *f.*

midday, merīdiēs, -ēī, *m.*

mind, animus, -ī, *m.*

mischief, inīquitās, -ātis, *f.*

miserable, miser, misera, miserum, *adj.*

mistress, domina, -ae, *f.*

mother, māter, mātris, *f.*

mountain, mōns, montis, *m.*

mouth, ōs, ōris, *n.*

move, moveō, -ēre, mōvī, mōtum

much, multus, -a, -um, *adj.*

much, multum, *adv.*

must, dēbeō, -ēre, dēbuī, dēbitum + *inf.*

my, meus, -a, -um, *possessive adj.*

N

name, nōmen, -inis, *n.*

near, prope, *prep. + acc.*

neglect, neglegō, -ere, neglēxī, neglēctum

never, numquam, *adv.*

new, novus, -a, -um, *adj.*

nice, pulcher, pulchra, pulchrum, *adj.*

night, nox, noctis, *f.*

no, minimē, *adv.*

nor, nec, *conj.*

not, nōn, *negative adv.*

not only . . . , but also . . . , nōn sōlum . . . , sed etiam . . .

not want, nōlō, *irregular verb*

nothing, nihil, *negative pronoun*

nourish, alō, -ere, aluī, altum/alitum

now, nunc, *adv.*

O

observe, cōnspiciō, -ere, -spexī, -spectum

often, saepe, *adv.*

old, vetustus, -a, -um, *adj.*

old age, senectūs, -ūtis, *f.*

old man, senex, -is, *m.*

on, in, *prep. + abl.*

on account of, propter, *prep. + acc.*

on behalf of, prō, *prep. + abl.*

only, tantum, *adv.*

open, iūstus, -a, -um, *adj.*

oracle, ōrāculum, -ī, *n.*

order, iussus, -ūs, *m.*

order somebody to do something, iubeō, -ēre, iussī, iussum + *acc. + inf.*

other, alius, alia, aliud, *adj.*

ought, dēbeō, -ēre, dēbuī, dēbitum + *inf.*

our, noster, nostra, nostrum, *possessive adj.*

out of, ē *or* ex, *prep. + abl.*

outside, forīs, *adv.*

outward, externus, -a, -um, *adj.*

overcome, vincō, -ere, vīcī, victum

overwhelm, opprimō, -ere, oppressī, oppressum

owe, dēbeō, -ēre, dēbuī, dēbitum

P

pain, dolor, -ōris, *m.*

parent, parēns, parentis, *m./f.*

part, pars, partis, *f.*

particle added to the first word of an interrogative sentence, -ne

passages of a book, locī, locōrum, *m. pl.*

peace, pāx, pācis, *f.*

people, hominēs, hominum, *m. pl.*

perhaps, fortasse, *adv.*

pet, dēliciae, -ārum, *f. pl.*

place, locus, locī, *m. (noun)*

place, pōnō, -ere, posuī, positum *(verb)*

plan, cōnsilium, -ī, *n.*

plant, herba, -ae, *f.*

play, lūdō, -ere, lūsī, lūsum

please, dēlectō (1)

poet, poēta, -ae, *m.*

poison, venēnum, -ī, *n.*

poor, pauper, pauperis, *adj.*

possess, possideō, -ēre, possēdī, possessum

prepare, parō (1)

preserve, servō (1)

proof, argūmentum, -ī, *n.*

public office or distinction, honor, -ōris, *m.*

punish, pūniō, -īre, pūnīvī, pūnītum

put, pōnō, -ere, posuī, positum

Q

queen, rēgīna, -ae, *f.*

R

raise, tollō, -ere, sustulī, sublātum

read, legō, -ere, lēgī, lēctum

reason, causa, -ae, *f.*

rebuke, reprehendō, -ere, -prehendī, -prehēnsum

receive, accipiō, -ere, -cēpī, -ceptum

red, ruber, rubra, rubrum, *adj.*

regard, aestimō (1)

remain, maneō, -ēre, mānsī, mānsum

renowned, celeber, -bris, -bre, *adj.*

reward, praemium, -ī, *n.*

rich, dīves, dīvitis, *adj.*

riches, dīvitiae, -ārum, *f. pl.*

right hand, dextra, -ae, *f.*

road, via, -ae, *f.*

rock, saxum, -ī, *n.*

Roman, Rōmānus, -a, -um, *adj.*

Rome, Rōma, -ae, *f.*

rouse, excitō (1)

rub, terō, -ere, trīvī, trītum

run, currō, -ere, cucurrī, cursum

run away, fugiō, -ere, fūgī, ——

rural, rūsticus, -a, -um, *adj.*

rush at, petō, -ere, petīvī, petītum

rustic, rūsticus, -a, -um, *adj.*

S

(s)/he/it, is, ea, id, *personal pronoun*

sad, miser, misera, miserum, *adj.*

sail, nāvigō (1)

sailor, nauta, -ae, *m.*

save, servō (1)

say, dīcō, -ere, dīxī, dictum

say/said, inquam (*only introducing direct speech*); **s/he says/said,** inquit (*only introducing direct speech*)

sea, mare, maris, *n.*

search, quaerō, -ere, quaesīvī, quaesītum

see, videō, -ēre, vīdī, vīsum

seek, petō, -ere, petīvī, petītum

seem, videor

seize, corripiō, -ere, -ripuī, -reptum

send, mittō, -ere, mīsī, missum

separate, sēparō (1)

serious, sevērus, -a, -um, *adj.*

severe, sevērus, -a, -um, *adj.*

shadows, tenebrae, -ārum, *f. pl.*

she, is, ea, id, *personal pronoun*

she-wolf, lupa, -ae, *f.*

ship, nāvis, -is, *f.*

shore, lītus, -oris, *n.*

should, dēbeō, -ēre, dēbuī, dēbitum + *inf.*

show, ostendō, -ere, ostendī, ostentum

similar, similis, -e, *adj.* + *gen.* or + *dat.*

sister, soror, -ōris, *f.*

sit, sedeō, -ēre, sēdī, sessum

skin, pellis, -is, *f.*

sky, caelum, -ī, *n.*

sleep, somnus, -ī, *m.*

sleep, dormiō, -īre, dormīvī, dormītum

small, parvus, -a, -um, *adj.*

smoke, fūmus, -ī, *m.*

snatch away, ēripiō, -ere, -ripuī, -reptum

so great, tantus, -a, -um, *adj.*

so, tam, *adv.;* ita, *adv.*

soldier, mīles, -itis, *m.*

son, fīlius, -ī, *m.*

soon, mox, *adv.*

soul, animus, -ī, *m.*

sparrow, passer, -eris, *m.*

speech, ōrātiō, -ōnis, *f.*

spirit, animus, -ī, *m.*

stand, stō, -āre, stetī, statum

stir up, excitō (1)

stone, saxum, -ī, *n.*

storm, tempestās, -ātis, *f.*

story, fābula, -ae, *f.*

stream, rīvus, -ī, *m.*

strength, vīs, ——— *f.; pl.* vīrēs, vīrium

strengthen, firmō (1)

strict, sevērus, -a, -um, *adj.*

strong, fortis, -e, *adj.*

study, studeō, -ēre, studuī, ——— + *dat.*

suddenly, subitō, *adv.*

suppress, opprimō, -ere, oppressī, oppressum

swiftly, celeriter, *adv.*

sword, gladius, -ī, *m.*

T

take, capiō, -ere, cēpī, captum; dūcō, -ere, dūxī, ductum

take back, recipiō, -ere, -cēpī, -ceptum

take care of, cūrō (1)

teach, doceō, -ēre, docuī, doctum

tear, lacrima, -ae, *f.*

tell, nārrō (1)

temple, templum, -ī, *n.*

terrifying, terribilis, -e, *adj.*

that, ille, illa, illud, *demonstrative pronoun and adj.;* is, ea, id, *demonstrative pronoun and adj.*

that, quī, quae, quod, *relative pronoun*

theft, fūrtum, -ī, *n.*

their, suus, -a, -um, *possessive adj.;* eōrum, *pronoun*

themselves, sē, *acc. of the reflexive pronoun*

then, deinde, *adv.;* tum, *adv.;* tunc, *adv.*

there, ibi, *adv.*

therefore, igitur, *conj.*

thief, fūr, fūris, *m.*

thing, rēs, reī, *f.*

think, cōgitō (1); putō (1)

this, hic, haec, hoc, *demonstrative pronoun and adj.;* is, ea, id, *demonstrative pronoun and adj.*

through, per, *prep.* + *acc.*

throw, iaciō, -ere, iēcī, iactum

time, tempus, -oris, *n.*

to, ad, *prep.* + *acc.;* in, *prep.* + *acc.*

together, ūnā, *adv.*

touch, tangō, -ere, tetigī, tāctum

toward, ad, *prep.* + *acc.*

tree, arbor, -oris, *f.*

trickery, dolus, -ī, *m.*

true, vērus, -a, -um, *adj.*

try, temptō (1)

turn, versō (1)

U

uncle, avunculus, -ī, *m.*

understand, intellegō, -ere, intellēxī, intellēctum

uproar, tumultus, -ūs, *m.*

V

vegetation, herba, -ae, *f.*

very, valdē, *adv.*

villa, vīlla, -ae, *f.*

voyage, nāvigō (1)

W

wage war, bellum gerō

wait for, exspectō (1)

wake up, excitō (1)

walk, ambulō (1)

wall, wall-fence, mūrus, -ī, *m.*

wander, errō (1)

want, cupiō, -ere, -īvī, -ītum

war, bellum, -ī, *n.*

water, aqua, -ae, *f.*

we, nōs, *personal pronoun*

wealth, dīvitiae, -ārum, *f. pl.*

weapons, arma, -ōrum, *n. pl.*

wear out, terō, -ere, trīvī, trītum

weather, caelum, -ī, *n.*

well, bene, *adv.*

well-known, celeber, -bris, -bre, *adj.*

what?, quid?, *interrogative pronoun;* quod?, *interrogative adj.*

wheel, rota, -ae, *f.*

when, cum, *conj.*

which, quī, quae, quod, *relative pronoun*

which?, quī, quae, quod?, *interrogative adjective*

while, dum, *conj.*

white, albus, -a, -um, *adj.*

who, quī, quae, quod, *relative pronoun*

who?, quis?, *interrogative pronoun*

why, cūr, *adj.*

wife, uxor, -ōris, *f.*

wind, ventus, -ī, *m.*

with, cum, *prep.* + *abl.*

with all one's might, prō vīribus

with me, mēcum

with you, tēcum

without, sine, *prep.* + *abl.*

wolf, *see she-wolf*

woman, fēmina, -ae, *f.;* mulier, -ieris, *f.*

word, verbum, -ī, *n.*

worship, colō, -ere, coluī, cultum

wound, vulnus, -eris, *n.* (noun)

wound, vulnerō (1) (verb)

wretched, miser, -a, -um, *adj.*

Y

yes, ita, *adv.*

you (pl.), vōs, *personal pronoun*

you (sg.), tū, *personal pronoun*

young lady, young man, adulēscēns, -entis, *m./f.*

your, yours (pl.), vester, vestra, vestrum, *possessive adj.*

your, yours (sg.), tuus, -a, -um, *possessive adj.*

LATIN TO ENGLISH GLOSSARY

This glossary contains the **Vocabulary to Learn*** as well as the **Reading Vocabulary** from all the chapters.

*All words from the **Vocabulary to Learn** are asterisked and coded, e.g., C12 means the word first appeared as **Vocabulary to Learn** in Chapter 12. In a very few instances, an additional meaning for the word is given in a later part of the text. Such additional meanings appear in the Glossary and when the additional meaning is part of the **Vocabulary to Learn**, the chapter introducing that additional meaning is also noted.

LIST OF ABBREVIATIONS:

(1) = first conjugation
abl. = ablative
acc. = accusative
adj. = adjective
adv. = adverb
conj. = conjunction
dat. = dative
f. = feminine

gen. = genitive
inf. = infinitive
interj. = interjection
m. = masculine
n. = neuter
pl. = plural
prep. = preposition
sg. = singular

NOTE:

The genitive of second declension words ending in *-ius* or *-ium* is indicated with a single *-ī*, which is the genitive ending itself. Note that in the full form of the genitive there is normally a double *i*: *fīlius, -ī* (= *fīliī*); *gaudium, -ī* (= *gaudiī*).

A

ā *or* **ab**, *prep.* + *abl.*, by, from, away from* C5

absum, abesse, āfuī, ——, to be absent, away

abundō (1) + *abl.*, to abound with* C20

accipiō, -ere, -cēpī, -ceptum, to accept, receive* C21

accurrō, -ere, -currī, -cursum, to run up

accūsō (1) + *acc.* + *gen.*, to accuse someone of something* C21

ācer, ācris, ācre, *adj.,* keen, fierce* C10

ad tempus, for the time being, for a while

ad, *prep.* + *acc.,* toward, to, into* C4

adolēscō, -ere, adolēvī, adultum, to grow up

adulēscēns, -entis, *m./f.,* young man, young lady* C20

aedificō (1), to build* C10

Aenēās, Aenēae (*gen.*), **Aenēae** (*dat.*), **Aenēam/ān** (*acc.*), **Aenēā** (*abl.*), *m.,* Aeneas, Trojan refugee, legendary founder of Roman race

aequus, -a, -um, *adj.,* even; **aequō animō,** indifferently* C20

Aeschinus, -ī, *m.,* Aeschinus

aestimō (1), to regard, esteem; **aestimō ūnīus assis,** I do not care a bit* C7

ager, agrī, *m.,* field* C3

agō, -ere, ēgī, āctum, to drive, lead, do, behave* C11

agricola, -ae, *m.,* farmer* C1

albus, -a, -um, *adj.,* white* C14

aliēnus, -a, -um, *adj.* + *prep.* ā/ab + *abl.,* foreign to, inconsistent with* C21

alius, alia, aliud, *adj.,* another, other* C13

alō, -ere, aluī, altum/alitum, to feed, nourish* C17

amāns, amantis, *m./f.,* lover

ambulō (1), to walk* C2

amīcus, -ī, *m.,* friend* C3

āmittō, -ere, -mīsī, -missum, to lose* C17

amō (1), to love* C2

amor, -ōris, *m.,* love* C7

Amūlius, -ī, *m.,* Amulius

angustus, -a, -um, *adj.,* narrow

animal, -ālis, *n.,* animal* C9

animus, -ī, *m.,* spirit, soul, mind* C3

ante, *prep.* + *acc.,* in front of* C15

antequam, *conj.,* before

Apollō, Apollinis, *m.,* Apollo, god of the sun, poetry, light, music

appropinquō (1), to approach

apud, *prep.* + *acc.,* at the house of* C13

aqua, -ae, *f.,* water* C1

arbor, -oris, *f.,* tree* C14

ārdeō, -ēre, ārsī, ——, to burn, be on fire* C11

argūmentum, -ī, *n.,* proof, indication, argument* C15

arma, -ōrum, *n. pl.,* weapons* C9

armātus, -a, -um, *adj.,* armed* C4

asportō (1), to carry away

at, *conj.,* but

Athēniēnsēs, Athēniēnsium, *m. pl.,* the Athenians

āthlēta, -ae, *m.,* athlete* C1

atque, *conj.,* and* C13

attonitus, -a, -um, *adj.,* astounded

auctōritās, -ātis, *f.,* authority

audiō, -īre, audīvī, audītum, to hear, listen* C9

autem, *conj.,* however* C4

auxilium, -ī, *n.,* help* C5

avunculus, -ī, *m.,* uncle* C16

axis, -is, *m.,* axle, axis* C21

B

barba, -ae, *f.,* beard* C19

bellum, -ī, *n.,* war* C4; **bellō iūstō,** through open warfare

belua, -ae, *f.,* beast

bene, *adv.,* well* C1

bonus, -a, -um, *adj.,* good* C4

bracchium, -ī, *n.,* arm

C

cadō, -ere, cecidī, cāsum, to fall* C14

caelum, -ī, *n.,* sky, heaven, weather* C16

calidus, -a, -um, *adj.,* hot

callidus, -a, -um, *adj.,* clever, cunning

capiō, -ere, cēpī, captum, to take, adopt, capture; **cōnsilia capere,** to make plans* C10

caput, -itis, *n.,* head* C9

carō, carnis, *f.,* meat, flesh* C19

Carthāgine, at Carthage, in Carthage

Carthāgō, -inis, *f.,* Carthage

casa, -ae, *f.,* little house, cottage* C3

castra, -ōrum, *n. pl.,* camp* C4

Catilīna, -ae, *m.,* Catiline, a bankrupt revolutionary whose plot to overthrow the Republic was exposed by Cicero

Catullus, -ī, *m.,* Catullus, Roman poet

causa, -ae, *f.,* cause, reason* C16

celeber, -bris, -bre, *adj.,* renowned, well-known, crowded* C10

celeriter, *adv.,* swiftly* C19

cibus, -ī, *m.,* food

cicātrīx, cicātrīcis, *f.,* scar

Cicero, -ōnis, *m.,* Cicero, Roman political figure of the first century BCE

cinis, -eris, *m.,* ash* C16

circum, *prep. + acc.,* around* C21

circus, -ī, *m.,* circus, often referring to the Circus Maximus in particular

cīvis, -is, *m./f.,* citizen* C9

clādēs, -is, *f.,* disaster* C16

clam, *adv.,* secretly

clāmor, -ōris, *m.,* shout, cry

classis, -is, *f.,* fleet* C16

claudō, -ere, clausī, clausum, to lock up

clīvus, -ī, *m.,* hill

cōgitō (1), to think* C5

cōgnōscō, -ere, -nōvī, -nitum, to recognize, get to know

colō, -ere, coluī, cultum, to worship, cultivate* C18

comedō, -ere, -ēdī, -ēsum, to eat* C14

coniūrātiō, -ōnis, *f.,* plot

cōnsilium, -ī, *n.,* plan* C5

cōnspiciō, -ere, -spexī, -spectum, to look at, observe* C11

cōnstantia, -ae, *f.,* constancy* C21

cōnsul, -ulis, *m.,* consul* C9

cōnsultō, *adv.,* on purpose

cōnsūmō, -ere, -sūmpsī, -sūmptum, to consume* C12

contrā, *prep. + acc.,* against* C8

conveniō, -īre, -vēnī, -ventum, to meet* C14

coquō, -ere, coxī, coctum, to cook* C19

cor, cordis, *n.,* heart* C20

cornū, -ūs, *n.,* horn* C17

corpus, -oris, *n.,* body* C9

corripiō, -ere, -ripuī, -reptum, to seize, engulf* C17

crēdō, -ere, crēdidī, crēditum + *dat.,* to believe somebody* C9

crēscō, -ere, crēvī, ——, to grow* C19

crūdēlis, -e, *adj.,* cruel* C11

Ctēsiphō, -ōnis, *m.,* Ctesipho

cum ... tum ..., both ... and ...

cum, *conj.,* when, after* C18

cum, *prep. + abl.,* with* C3

Cupīdō, Cupīdinis, *m.,* Cupid (in Greek, Eros)

cupiō, -ere, -īvī, -ītum, to desire, want* C10

cūr, *adv.,* why?* C15

cūria, -ae, *f.,* senate (building)

cūrō (1), to care for, take care of* C2

currō, -ere, cucurrī, cursum, to run* C17

D

dē, *prep. + abl.,* about, concerning, down from* C5

dea, -ae, *f.,* goddess* C18

dēbeō, -ēre, dēbuī, dēbitum + *inf.,* ought, must, should; to owe* C2

dēcernō, -ere, -crēvī, -crētum + *inf.,* to decide, determine* C8

deinde, *adv.,* then* C3

dēlectō (1), to delight, please* C20

dēleō, -ēre, dēlēvī, dēlētum, to destroy* C10

dēliciae, -ārum, *f. pl.,* delight, pet* C7

Delphicus, -a, -um, *adj.,* belonging to Delphi, Delphic

Delphīs, at Delphi

Dēmea, -ae, *m.,* Demea

dēns, dentis, *m.,* tooth

dēscendō, -ere, -scendī, -scēnsum, to descend* C21

deus, -ī, *m.,* god* C10

dēvastō (1), to devastate* C17

dextra, -ae, *f.,* right hand* C12

dīcō, -ere, dīxī, dictum, to say* C8

Dīdō, Dīdōnis, *f.,* Dido, exile from Phoenician Tyre, founding queen of Carthage

diēs, diēī, *m./f.,* day* C18

difficilis, -e, *adj.,* difficult* C15

digitus, -ī, *m.,* finger* C7

discēdō, -ere, -cessī, -cessum, to leave, go away* C13

discō, -ere, didicī, ——, to learn

diū, *adv.,* for a long time* C2

dīves, dīvitis, *adj.,* rich* C13

dīvīnus, -a, -um, *adj.,* divine* C20

dīvitiae, -ārum, *f. pl.,* wealth, riches* C21

dō, dāre, dedī, dătum, to give* C4

doceō, -ēre, docuī, doctum, to teach* C6

doctus, -a, -um, *adj.,* learned* C13

doleō, -ēre, doluī, ——, to feel pain, hurt* C5

dolor, -ōris, *m.,* grief, pain* C11

dolus, -ī, *m.,* trickery, deception* C4

domī, at home* C3

domina, -ae, *f.,* mistress* C7

domus, -ūs, *f.,* house, home* C17

dōnum, -ī, *n.,* gift* C10

dormiō, -īre, dormīvī, dormītum, to sleep* C18

Druidēs, -um, *m. pl.,* the Druids

dūcō, -ere, dūxī, ductum, to lead, take* C13

dulcissime rērum, dear fellow, literally "the sweetest of all things"

dum, *conj.,* while* C6

duo, duae, dua, *numeral,* two

dux, ducis, *m.,* leader, general* C8

E

ē *or* **ex,** *prep. + abl.,* from, out of* C4

ecce, *interj.,* look here! * C15

egeō, -ēre, eguī, ——— + abl., to lack something* C20

egestās, -ātis, *f.,* lack, poverty

ego, *personal pronoun,* I* C3

ēiciō, -ere, ēiēcī, ēiectum, to throw away

enim, *conj.,* for, in fact* C13

eō diē, on that day

epistula, -ae, *f.,* letter* C5

equus, -ī, *m.,* horse* C10

ēripiō, -ere, -ripuī, -reptum, to snatch away* C21

errō (1), to wander, make a mistake* C21

et, *conj.,* and* C1

etiam, *adv.,* even, also* C15

Etrūscus, -a, -um, *adj.,* Etruscan

ēvānēscō, -ere, ēvanuī, ———, to disappear

excitō (1), to awaken, wake up, rouse, stir up* C18

exclāmō (1), to exclaim* C18

excutiō, -ere, -cussī, -cussum, to shake off

exemplar, -āris, *n.,* example* C9

exemplum, -ī, *n.,* example* C6

exeunt, they exit, go out

eximō, -ere, -ēmī, -ēmptum, to take out

exspectō (1), to wait for, await, expect* C2

exstinguō, -ere, exstīnxī, exstīnctum, to extinguish* C17

externus, -a, -um, *adj.,* outward, external* C21

F

Fābricius, -ī, *m.,* Fabricius

fābula, -ae, *f.,* story* C2

faciēs, -ēī, *f.,* face* C18

facile, *adv.,* easily* C17

faciō, -ere, fēcī, factum, to do, make* C12

familia, -ae, *f.,* family, household* C5

fātum, -ī, *n.,* fate, destiny* C18

fax, fācis, *f.,* torch

Fēlīciō, ———, *m.,* Felicio, a servant's name

fēlīx, -īcis, *adj.,* fortunate, happy* C10

fēmina, -ae, *f.,* woman* C16

femur, femoris, *n.,* the upper leg, the thigh

ferōx, -ōcis, *adj.,* fierce, ferocious* C19

ferus, -a, -um, *adj.,* wild, savage

fīlia, -ae, *f.,* daughter* C1

fīlius, -ī, *m.,* son* C3

firmō (1), to strengthen* C6

flamma, -ae, *f.,* flame* C10

flexus, -a, -um, *adj.,* curved

fluō, -ere, flūxī, fluxum, to flow* C14

folium, -ī, *n.,* leaf

forīs, *adv.,* outside, in the open* C19

fōrma, -ae, *f.,* form, appearance* C2

fortasse, *adv.,* perhaps* C15

fortis, -e, *adj.,* brave, strong* C10

fortitūdō, -inis, *f.,* courage* C8

fortūna, -ae, *f.,* fortune, the goddess Fortune* C21

frāter, frātris, *m.,* brother

fugiō, -ere, fūgī, ———, to flee, run away* C10

fūmus, -ī, *m.,* smoke* C16

fūnestus, -a, -um, *adj.,* deadly* C16

fūr, fūris, *m.,* thief* C20

fūrtum, -ī, *n.,* theft* C20

futūrus, -a, -um, *participle,* about to be* C21

G

Gallī, -ōrum, *m. pl.,* the Gauls, the inhabitants of France

gaudium, -ī, *n.,* joy* C5

gerō, -ere, gessī, gestum, to carry; **sē gerit,** (s)/he behaves* C9; *with clothing or articles of clothing as its object,* to wear; **bellum gerere,** to wage war* C12

gladius, -ī, *m.,* sword* C14

Graecia, -ae, *f.,* Greece

Graecus, -a, -um, *adj.,* Greek; **Graecī, -ōrum,** *m. pl.,* the Greeks

gremium, -ī, *n.,* bosom, lap* C7

gutta, -ae, *f.,* drop

H

habeō, -ēre, habuī, habitum, to have* C2

habitō (1), to live, dwell* C2

hāc nocte, tonight

herba, -ae, *f.,* plant, vegetation* C19

heus!, hey!

hic, haec, hoc, *demonstrative pronoun and adj.,* this, latter* C19

homō, -inis, *m.,* man (i.e., human being); *pl.* people* C8

honor, -ōris, *m.,* honor, public office or distinction* C21

hostis, -is, *m.,* enemy* C10

hūc atque illūc, hither and thither, to and fro

hūmānus, -a, -um, *adj.,* human* C20

Hūnī, -ōrum, *m. pl.,* the Huns

I

iaceō, -ēre, iacuī, ———, to lie down, be inert* C6

iaciō, -ere, iēcī, iactum, to throw* C17

iam, *adv.,* already* C14

iānua, -ae, *f.,* door

ibi, *adv.,* there* C12

igitur, *conj.,* therefore* C16

ignis, -is, *m.,* fire* C12

ille, illa, illud, *demonstrative pronoun and adj.,* that, former* C20

illūc, *adv.,* to that place, thither

imparātus, -a, -um, *adj.,* unprepared

impedīmentum, -ī, *n.,* impediment

imperātor, -ōris, *m.,* emperor, general* C17

impetus, -ūs, *m.,* impetus, force, attack* C17

importūnus, -a, -um, *adj.,* boorish

improbus, -a, -um, *adj.,* bad, wicked

in, *prep. + abl.,* in, on* C3

in, *prep. + acc.,* into, to* C4

incendium, -ī, *n.,* conflagration, eruption* C16

industria, -ae, *f.,* industry, care

inīquitās, -ātis, *f.,* injustice, mischief* C20

inīquus, -a, -um, *adj.,* unjust

initium, -ī, *n.,* beginning* C17

inquam, I say/I said (*only introducing direct speech*)* C15

inquit, (s)/he says or said (*only introducing direct speech*)* C12

intellegō, -ere, intellēxī, intellēctum, to understand* C8

inter, *prep. + acc.,* between, among* C19

intereā, *adv.,* meanwhile

intrō (1), to enter* C4

inūsitātus, -a, -um, *adj.,* strange, unusual

invideō, -ēre, invīdī, invīsum + *dat.,* to envy someone* C7

invīsō, -ere, invīsī, invīsum, to visit

ipse, ipsa, ipsum, *demonstrative pronoun and adj.,* -self

īra, -ae, *f.,* anger* C12

is, ea, id, *personal and demonstrative pronoun and adj.,* (s)/he/it, this, that* C12

ita, *adv.,* so, in such a way* C18; yes* C11

Italia, -ae, *f.,* Italy

itaque, *conj.,* and so* C1

iubeō, -ēre, iussī, iussum + *acc. + inf.,* to order somebody to do something* C4

iūdex, -icis, *m.,* judge* C13

iūdicō (1), to judge* C6

Iuppiter, Iovis, *m.,* Jupiter, king of gods (in Greek, Zeus)

iussus, -ūs, *m.,* order (*usually employed in the ablative singular only*)* C17

iūstus, -a, -um, *adj.,* legitimate, just, open* C4

L

lacrima, -ae, *f.,* tear* C5

laqueus, -ī, *m.,* noose, lasso

leaena, -ae, *f.,* lioness

legō, -ere, lēgī, lēctum, to read, choose* C16

lēx, lēgis, *f.,* law* C20

liber, librī, *m.,* book* C6

līberō (1) + *acc. + abl.,* to free someone from something* C8

licet + *dat. + inf.,* it is allowed, it is permitted for someone to do something* C13

ligneus, -a, -um, *adj.,* wooden

littera, -ae, *f.,* letter of the alphabet; **litterae, -ārum,** *f. pl.,* literature, letter (epistle)* C6

lītus, -oris, *n.,* shore* C16

locus, -ī, *m.,* place; **locī, -ōrum,** *m. pl.,* passages of a book; **loca, -ōrum,** *n. pl.,* geographical places* C17

longē, *adv.,* far* C5

longus, -a, -um, *adj.,* long* C5

Lūcīlius, -ī, *m.,* Lucilius, a friend of Seneca's to whom he addressed his philosophical essays in the form of letters

lūculentus, -a, -um, *adj.,* splendid

lūdō, -ere, lūsī, lūsum, to play* C20

lūmen, -inis, *n.,* light

lupa, -ae, *f.,* she-wolf* C1

M

Maecēnās, Maecēnātis, *m.,* Maecenas, friend of Augustus, patron of the arts

magnus, -a, -um, *adj.,* large, great, important* C4

maior, maius, *adj.,* bigger, greater

male, *adv.,* badly

malitia, -ae, *f.,* badness, wickedness

malus, -a, -um, *adj.,* bad* C4

maneō, -ēre, mānsī, mānsum, to remain* C6

manus, -ūs, *f.,* hand* C17

Mārcus Tullius Cicero, Mārcī Tulliī Ciceronis, *m.,* Marcus Tullius Cicero

mare, maris, *n.,* sea* C9

marītus, -ī, *m.,* husband* C18

Mārs, -tis, *m.,* Mars, the god of war (in Greek, Ares)

māter, mātris, *f.,* mother* C16

mēcum = cum mē, with me* C13

mellītus, -a, -um, *adj.,* sweet as honey

memoria, -ae, *f.,* memory* C6

Menaechmus, -ī, *m.,* Menaechmus; **Menaechmī, -ōrum,** *m. pl.,* the brothers Menaechmi

mercimōnium, -ī, *n.,* merchandise

Mercurius, -ī, *m.,* Mercury, messenger god, patron of merchants, travelers, thieves (in Greek, Hermes)

merīdiēs, -ēī, *m.,* midday* C18

meus, -a, -um, *possessive adj.,* my* C7

mīles, -itis, *m.,* soldier* C8

minimē, *adv.,* no* C11

Mīsēnum, -ī, *n.,* a base for the imperial Roman navy in the Bay of Naples; **Mīsēnī,** at Misenum

miser, misera, miserum, *adj.,* wretched, miserable, sad* C5

mittō, -ere, mīsī, missum, to send* C11

mōns, montis, *m.,* mountain* C16

mordeō, -ēre, momordī, morsum, to bite

mors, mortis, *f.,* death* C9

mortuus, -a, -um, *adj.,* dead

moveō, -ēre, mōvī, mōtum, to move* C10

mox, *adv.,* soon* C14

Mūcius Scaevola, Mūciī Scaevolae, *m.,* Mucius Scaevola

mulier, -ieris, *f.,* woman* C9

multum, *adv.,* much* C18

multus, -a, -um, *adj.,* much, many* C6

mūnīmentum, -ī, *n.,* protection, fortification

mūrus, -ī, *m.,* wall, wall-fence* C17

mūtō (1), to change* C21

N

nam, *conj.,* for, in fact* C5

nārrō (1), to tell* C2

nātūra, -ae, *f.,* nature

nauta, -ae, *m.,* sailor* C1

nāvigō (1), to sail, voyage* C8

nāvis, -is, *f.,* ship* C16

-ne, a particle added to the first word of an interrogative sentence* C11

nec, *conj.,* and not, nor* C10

necō (1), to kill

neglegō, -ere, neglēxī, neglēctum, to neglect* C15

nēminī, to nobody

Nerō, Nerōnis, *m.,* Nero, Julio-Claudian emperor

nihil, *negative pronoun,* nothing* C13

nisi, *conj.,* if not, unless

nōbīscum = cum nōbīs

noctū, *adv.,* during the night* C20

nōlō, *irregular verb,* not to want, be unwilling* C13

nōmen, -inis, *n.,* name* C12

nōn, *negative adv.,* not* C2

nōn sōlum . . ., sed etiam . . ., not only . . ., but also . . .* C5

nōnne?, don't you?

nōs, *personal pronoun,* we* C12

noster, nostra, nostrum, *possessive adj.,* our* C12

nōtus, -a, -um, *adj.,* known

novus, -a, -um, *adj.,* new* C11

nox, noctis, *f.,* night* C10

nūbēs, -is, *f.,* cloud* C16

nūgae, -ārum, *f. pl.,* trifles

num?, do I? (negative answer implied)

numquam, *adv.,* never* C16

nunc, *adv.,* now* C2

O

ō, *interj.,* oh!

occīdō, -ere, occīdī, occīsum, to kill* C12

occultātus, -a, -um, *adj.,* hidden

occultō (1), to hide* C18

occultus, -a, -um, *adj.,* hidden

oculus, -ī, *m.,* eye* C7

odium, -ī, *n.,* hatred* C14

oleum, -ī, *n.,* oil

omnis, -e, *adj.,* each, every, all* C13

opprimō, -ere, oppressī, oppressum, to overwhelm, suppress* C16

oppugnō (1), to attack

ōrāculum, -ī, *n.,* oracle* C8

ōrātiō, -ōnis, *f.,* speech; **ōrātiōnem habēre,** to make a speech* C9

ōs, ōris, *n.,* mouth* C14

ostendō, -ere, ostendī, ostentum, to show* C12

P

paene, *adv.,* almost* C20

papae!, wow!

parātus, -a, -um, *adj.,* prepared (often + *inf.*)

parēns, -rentis, *m./f.,* parent* C14

pariēs, parietis, *m.,* wall

parō (1), to prepare, get ready* C2; design* C5

pars, partis, *f.,* part* C16

parvus, -a, -um, *adj.,* small* C15

passer, -eris, *m.,* sparrow* C7

pater, -tris, *m.,* father* C18

patria, -ae, *f.,* fatherland* C2

paucī, -ae, -a, *adj.,* few* C10

paulisper, *adv.,* for a little while

pauper, pauperis, *adj.,* poor* C20

pāx, pācis, *f.,* peace* C9

pectus, -oris, *n.,* chest* C14

pellis, -is, *f.,* skin, hide* C19

per, *prep. + acc.,* through* C14

perīculum, -ī, *n.,* danger* C10

permoveō, -ēre, -mōvī, -mōtum, to perturb

Persae, -ārum, *m. pl.,* the Persians

petō, -ere, petīvī, petītum, to seek, head for, go to, rush at* C8

piger, pigra, pigrum, *adj.,* lazy

pīpiō, -āre, ——, ——, to chirp

pirum, -ī, *n.,* pear (fruit)

pirus, -ī, *f.,* pear tree

plēnus, -a, -um, *adj. + gen.* or *+ abl.,* full of* C20

pluit, -ere, pluit, ——, *an impersonal verb (used only in 3rd sg.),* to rain

plūs quam, more than

poena, -ae, *f.,* punishment

poēta, -ae, *m.,* poet* C1

pōmum, -ī, *n.,* fruit* C20

pōnō, -ere, posuī, positum, to put, place* C12

porcus, -ī, *m.,* pig

porta, -ae, *f.,* gate

possideō, -ēre, possēdī, possessum, to possess* C21

possum, posse, potuī, ——, to be able, can* C6

post, *prep. + acc.,* after* C18

posteā, *adv.,* afterward* C1

postquam, *conj.,* after* C19

praeclārus, -a, -um, *adj.,* famous, distinguished* C4

praefectus, -ī, *m.,* prefect, commander, chief

praemium, -ī, *n.,* reward* C4

prīmum, *adv.,* first

prīmus, -a, -um, *adj.,* first* C14

prō certō, *adverbial phrase,* for certain, for sure* C21

prō Iuppiter!, by Jove!

prō, *prep. + abl.,* for, on behalf of* C13

proelium, -ī, *n.,* battle, combat* C19

profuga, -ae, *m.,* deserter

prope, *prep. + acc.,* near* C12

propter, *prep. + acc.,* because of, on account of* C6

Psȳchē (gen. Psȳchēs, dat. Psȳchē, acc. Psȳchēn, abl. Psȳchē), *f.,* Psyche

puella, -ae, *f.,* girl* C1

puer, puerī, *m.,* boy* C3

pugnō (1), to fight* C10

pulcher, pulchra, pulchrum, *adj.,* beautiful, nice* C5

pulchritūdō, pulchritūdinis, *f.,* beauty

pūniō, -īre, pūnīvī, pūnītum, to punish* C20

putō (1), to think, consider* C7

Pȳramus, -ī, *m.,* Pyramus

Pyrrhus, -ī, *m.,* Pyrrhus, king of Epirus

Pȳthia, -ae, *f.,* the Pythian priestess, responsible for uttering the ambiguous oracles at the shrine of Apollo at Delphi, Greece

Q

quaerō, -ere, quaesīvī, quaesītum, to look for, search* C18

-que, *conj.,* and* C11

quī, quae, quod, *relative pronoun,* which, who, that* C14

quī, quae, quod?, *interrogative adj.,* which? what? * C15

quid agis, how are you?

quis, quid?, *interrogative pronoun,* who? what? * C13

quō?, to what place?

quōcum = **cum quō**, with whom

quōmodo, how?

quondam, *adv.,* once

quoque, *adv.,* also* C11

R

rādīx, rādīcis, *f.,* root

rāmus, -ī, *m.,* branch

recipiō, -ere, -cēpī, -ceptum, to take back* C21

rēgīna, -ae, *f.,* queen* C11

relinquō, -ere, relīquī, relictum, to leave behind, abandon* C11

Remus, -ī, *m.,* Remus, brother of Romulus

reparō (1), to repair

reprehendō, -ere, -prehendī, -prehēnsum, to blame, rebuke* C21

rērum nātūra, rērum nātūrae, *f.,* nature

rēs, reī, *f.,* thing, matter* C18

respondeō, -ēre, -spondī, -spōnsum, to answer* C13

reveniō, -īre, -vēnī, -ventum, to return

rēx, rēgis, *m.,* king* C8

Rhēa Silvia, Rhēae Silviae, *f.,* Rhea Silvia, vestal virgin

rīvus, -ī, *m.,* brook, stream* C3

rogō (1), to ask* C13

Rōma, -ae, *f.,* Rome* C1

Rōmānus, -a, -um, *adj.,* Roman* C4

Rōmulus, -ī, *m.,* Romulus, legendary founder of Rome

rota, -ae, *f.,* wheel* C21

ruber, rubra, rubrum, *adj.,* red* C14

rūsticus, -a, -um, *adj.,* rural, rustic* C15

S

sacer, sacra, sacrum, *adj.,* holy, sacred

sacra, -ōrum, *n. pl.,* religious rites

saepe, *adv.,* often* C6

sagitta, -ae, *f.,* arrow

salūtem plūrimam dīcit + *dat.,* (s)/he greets (someone) (a standard formula for beginning a letter). Literally it means "([s]/he) says (i.e., wishes) very much health (the best of health) to . . ."

salvē!, hello!

sanguis, sanguinis, *m.,* blood* C14

sānō (1), to heal* C19

saxum, -ī, *n.,* stone, rock* C15

scientia, -ae, *f.,* knowledge

sciō, scīre, scīvī, scītum, to know* C9

sē, *acc. of the reflexive pronoun,* herself, himself, itself, themselves* C7

sed, *conj.,* but* C4

sedeō, -ēre, sēdī, sessum, to sit* C19

sella, -ae, *f.,* seat, chair

sēmoveō, -ēre, sēmōvī, sēmōtum, to remove

semper, *adv.,* always* C5

Seneca, -ae, *m.,* Seneca, Roman author

senectūs, -ūtis, *f.,* old age* C15

senex, -is, *m.,* old man* C7

sentiō, -īre, sēnsī, sēnsum, to feel* C9

sēparō (1), to separate* C14

servō (1), to save, preserve* C6

sevērus, -a, -um, *adj.,* serious, strict, severe* C7

sī, *conj.,* if* C18

sīcut, *adv.,* just as* C15

silva, -ae, *f.,* forest* C11

similis, -e, *adj.* + *gen.* or + *dat.,* like, similar* C12

sine, *prep.* + *abl.,* without* C17

soleō, -ēre, solitus sum + *inf.,* to be accustomed* C6

sōlus, -a, -um, *adj.,* sole, only

somnus, -ī, *m.,* sleep* C18

soror, -ōris, *f.,* sister* C7

spectō (1), to look at, gaze, stare at

spēlunca, -ae, *f.,* cave* C11

statim, *adv.,* immediately* C12

stō, -āre, stetī, statum, to stand* C15

studeō, -ēre, studuī, —— + *dat.,* to study, be eager for, be interested in* C16

studiōsus, -a, -um, *adj.* + *gen.,* interested in, a student of

subitō, *adv.,* suddenly* C12

sum, esse, fuī, ——, to be* C6

summus, -a, -um, *adj.,* the top of

suus, -a, -um, *possessive adj.,* his, her, its, their* C13

Syrācūsānus, -a, -um, *adj.,* from Syracuse

T

taberna, -ae, *f.,* shop

tam, *adv.,* so* C18

tamen, *conj.,* however* C5

tamquam, *adv.,* as if

tandem, *adv.,* at last* C9

tangō, -ere, tetigī, tāctum, to touch* C14

tantum, *adv.,* only* C13

tantus, -a, -um, *adj.,* so great* C12

tēcum = **cum tē,** with you* C13

tempestās, -ātis, *f.,* storm* C11

templum, -ī, *n.,* temple* C8

temptō (1), to try* C17

tempus, -oris, *n.,* time* C9

tenebrae, -ārum, *f. pl.,* shadows, darkness* C6

teneō, -ēre, tenuī, tentum, to hold* C2

Terentia, -ae, *f.,* Terentia, wife of Cicero

terō, -ere, trīvī, trītum, to wear out, rub* C19

terra, -ae, *f.,* land* C1

terribilis, -e, *adj.,* terrifying* C19

tertius, -a, -um, *adj.,* third

Themistoclēs, Themistoclis, *m.,* Themistocles, Athenian general

Thisbē, Thisbēs (gen.), Thisbē (dat.), Thisbēn (acc.), Thisbē (voc.), *f.,* Thisbe

timeō, -ēre, timuī, ——, to fear, be afraid* C3

timor, -ōris, *m.,* fear* C8

tolerō (1), to tolerate, bear

tollō, -ere, sustulī, sublātum, to lift up, raise, destroy* C21

tonō, -āre, -uī, ——, to thunder

tōtus, -a, -um, *adj.,* whole

trāns Tiberim, on the other side of the Tiber River

trēs, tria, *numeral,* three

trīstitia, -ae, *f.,* sadness

Trōia, -ae, *f.,* Troy

Trōiānus, -a, -um, *adj.,* Trojan

tū, *personal pronoun,* you (sg.)* C3

tum, *adv.,* then* C13

tumultus, -ūs, *m.,* uproar, confusion* C17

tunc, *adv.,* then* C8

tuus, -a, -um, *possessive adj.,* yours, your (sg.)* C12

U

ubi, *adv.,* where

ubīque, *adv.,* everywhere* C15

Ulixes, Ulixis, *m.,* Odysseus, Ulysses (Latin)

ūllus, -a, -um, *adj.,* any* C21

umquam, *adv.,* ever* C15

ūnā, *adv.,* together* C11

ūnusquisque nostrum, each one of us

urbs, urbis, *f.,* city (usually the city of Rome)* C9

uxor, -ōris, *f.,* wife* C18

V

valdē, *adv.,* very, exceedingly* C3

valē!, goodbye!* C13

vectus, -a, -um, *adj.,* carried, driven

vēlāmen, vēlāminis, *n.,* veil

venēnum, -ī, *n.,* poison* C4

veniō, -īre, vēnī, ventum, to come* C9

ventus, -ī, *m.,* wind* C17

Venus, Veneris, *f.,* Venus, goddess of beauty and love (in Greek, Aphrodite)

verbum, -ī, *n.,* word* C7

versō (1), to turn* C21

vērus, -a, -um, *adj.,* true* C15

Vesta, -ae, *f.,* Vesta, goddess of the hearth (in Greek, Hestia)

vester, vestra, vestrum, *possessive adj.,* yours (*pl.*), your* C12

vestīmentum, -ī, *n.,* garment, (*pl.*) clothes* C19

Vesuvius, -ī, *m.,* (Mt.) Vesuvius

vetustus, -a, -um, *adj.,* old* C15

via, -ae, *f.,* road* C3

Via Sacra, a street in the Roman Forum

victōria, -ae, *f.,* victory

videō, -ēre, vīdī, vīsum, to see, (passive) seem* C2

vīlicus, -ī, *m.,* bailiff, steward

vīlla, -ae, *f.,* country house, villa* C15

vincō, -ere, vīcī, victum, to conquer, defeat* C8

vīnctus, -a, -um, *adj.,* bound, chained

vinculum, -ī, *n.,* chain, fetter* C4

vir, virī, *m.,* man* C3

vīs, ——, *f., pl.* **vīrēs, vīrium,** force, strength; **prō vīribus,** with all one's might* C12

vīta, -ae, *f.,* life* C6

vīvō, -ere, vīxī, victum, to live* C19

vocō (1), to call* C2

vōs, *personal pronoun,* you (*pl.*)* C12

vulnerō (1), to wound* C19

vulnus, -eris, *n.,* wound* C19

vult, he wishes

X

Xerxēs, Xerxis, *m.,* Xerxes, the great king of the Persians (who invaded Greece in 480 BCE)

ILLUSTRATION CREDITS

CHAPTER 1
Mars (© 2008 Jupiter Images Corp.)
Romulus and Remus Coin (© 2008 Shutterstock Images LLC)

CHAPTER 2
Greek Actor in a Mask (© 2008 Jupiter Images Corp.)
Roman Theatre in Mérida (© 2008 Shutterstock Images LLC)

CHAPTER 3
Actors in a Play (© 2008 Jupiter Images Corp.)
The Wolf and Lamb (© 2008 Jupiter Images Corp.)
Greek Mask (© 2008 Jupiter Images Corp.)

CHAPTER 4
Soldiers (© 2008 Jupiter Images Corp.)
Roman Leg Armor (© 2008 Jupiter Images Corp.)

CHAPTER 5
State of Kansas Seal (© 2008 Vector Images)
Statue of a Woman and Baby (© 2008 Jupiter Images Corp.)

CHAPTER 6
Children in School (© 2008 Jupiter Images Corp.)
Bust of Julius Caesar (© 2008 Jupiter Images Corp.)

CHAPTER 7
Mosaic of Pheasants (© 2008 Shutterstock Images LLC)
Romans in a Dining Room (© 2008 Jupiter Images Corp.)

CHAPTER 8
Xerxes with His Servants (© 2008 Jupiter Images Corp.)
Treasury at Delphi (© 2008 Shutterstock Images LLC)

CHAPTER 9
Rome Personified on a Republican Coin (© 2008 Shutterstock Images LLC)
Catilinarian Conspiracy (© 2008 Jupiter Images Corp.)

CHAPTER 10
Laocoön Sculpture (© 2008 Shutterstock Images LLC)
Ruins at Troy (© 2008 Jupiter Images Corp.)

CHAPTER 11
Dido and Aeneas (© 2008 Jupiter Images Corp.)
Dido Fresco (© 2008 Jupiter Images Corp.)

CHAPTER 12
Mucius and Fire (© 2008 Jupiter Images Corp.)
Etruscan Breastplate (© 2008 Jupiter Images Corp.)

CHAPTER 13
Roman Shield (© 2008 Jupiter Images Corp.)
Via Sacra (© 2008 Shutterstock Images LLC)

CHAPTER 14
Thisbe at the Wall (© 2008 Jupiter Images Corp.)
Ovid (© 2008 Jupiter Images Corp.)

CHAPTER 15
Seneca in the Bathtub (© 2008 Jupiter Images Corp.)
Villa of Diomedes (© 2008 Jupiter Images Corp.)
Tomb of Seneca (© 2008 Jupiter Images Corp.)

CHAPTER 16
Roman Ship (© 2008 Jupiter Images Corp.)
Cave Canem Mosaic (© 2008 Jupiter Images Corp.)
Skull Mosaic (© 2008 Shutterstock Images LLC)

CHAPTER 17
Assassination of Julius Caesar (© 2008 Jupiter Images Corp.)
Bust of Tiberius (© 2008 Jupiter Images Corp.)
Caligula (© 2008 Jupiter Images Corp.)

CHAPTER 18
Roman Banquet (© 2008 Jupiter Images Corp.)
Pompeiian Amphoras (© 2008 Jupiter Images Corp.)

CHAPTER 19
Huns on the March (© 2008 Jupiter Images Corp.)
Attila and the Huns (© 2008 Jupiter Images Corp.)
Attila the Hun (© 2008 Jupiter Images Corp.)

CHAPTER 20
St. Augustine (© 2008 Jupiter Images Corp.)
Dido and Aeneas (© 2008 Jupiter Images Corp.)

CHAPTER 21
Boethius (© 2008 Jupiter Images Corp.)